# PRIMARY MATHEMATICS

# Challenging
## Word Problems

**5**

SINGAPORE MATH® PROGRAM

### Yan Kow Cheong

**Marshall Cavendish** Education

US Distributor

SM Singapore Math Inc.®

© 2010 Panpac Education Private Limited
© 2011 Marshall Cavendish International (Singapore) Private Limited

This edition ©2014 Marshall Cavendish Education Pte Ltd
*(Formerly known as Marshall Cavendish International (Singapore) Private Limited)*

**Published by Marshall Cavendish Education**
Times Centre, 1 New Industrial Road, Singapore 536196
Customer Service Hotline: (65) 6213 9444
US Office Tel: (+1-914) 332 8888 | Fax: (+1-914) 332 8882
E-mail: tmesales@mceducation.com
Website: www.mceducation.com

Distributed by
**Singapore Math Inc.®**
19535 SW 129th Avenue
Tualatin, OR 97062, USA
Tel: (+1-503) 557 8100
Website: www.singaporemath.com

First published 2010
New edition 2014

Primary Mathematics (Common Core Edition) Challenging Word Problems 5
ISBN 978-981-01-8975-4

Printed in the United States of America

We would like to acknowledge contributions by:

**Primary Mathematics (Common Core Edition) Challenging Word Problems**
Jennifer Kempe (Curriculum Advisor from Singapore Math Inc.®)

# Preface

 **Common Core Edition** **Challenging Word Problems** provides graded exercises for students of mixed abilities and challenging questions for better math students. This series is written to supplement Singapore's **Primary Mathematics** textbooks (Common Core Edition) distributed by Singapore Math Inc.® for use in the USA.

Adopting a topical approach in which mathematical concepts and skills are taught and reinforced, the **Challenging Word Problems** series serves to improve students' problem-solving skills and enhance their mathematical reasoning.

Each book in the series features the following:

- **Worked Examples** for each topic show common methods of solution used in the Primary Mathematics textbooks;

- **Practice Questions** allow students to apply and practice questions similar to the ones discussed in the Worked Examples and in the Primary Mathematics textbooks;

- **Challenging Problems** provide opportunities for more capable students to solve higher-order word problems and further develop their problem-solving skills;

- **Review Questions** allow students to test their understanding of the concepts discussed in earlier topics and in the Primary Mathematics textbooks;

- **Answers** allow teachers or students to check their answers to all practice exercises and challenging problems;

- **Worked solutions** provide commonly used methods of solving non-routine questions, while encouraging creative or intuitive ones as well.

A student's guide to using the **Challenging Word Problems** series effectively.

1. Read each question given in the Worked Example. Try to solve it before reading the solution.

2. If your solution is similar to the one given in the Worked Example, well done. If you have used a different method, yet have arrived at the same answer, great—you now have at least two methods of solving this question.

3. If your answer is different, look at your work again and figure out where you may have gone wrong.

4. If you have understood all the worked examples, proceed to the Practice Questions; then check your answers with the ones at the back of the book. Should you get stuck at any question, don't panic; go through it again. If you still find difficulty in solving the question, seek help from your friend or teacher.

5. If you have understood and solved all the Practice Questions, you are now ready to try the Challenging Problems. Do them on your own first. Seek help only if you need some hints or clarification.

6. Try to come up with similar questions and challenge your friends to solve them. For a given question, discuss some possible solutions that you may have used in arriving at the answer.

# Contents

Blank

# 1 Whole Numbers

## Worked Example 1

Mrs. Jones has 33 coins. She gives them out one at a time to Ann, Beth, Corinne, Denise, and Ethel, who are seated around a table. She gives the first coin to Ann, the second coin to Beth, and so on until all the coins are given out. Who does she give the last coin to?

**Method 1**

| Ann | Beth | Corinne | Denise | Ethel |
|-----|------|---------|--------|-------|
| 1   | 2    | 3       | 4      | 5     |
| 6   | 7    | 8       | 9      | 10    |
| 11  | 12   | 13      | 14     | 15    |
| ⋮   | ⋮    | ⋮       | ⋮      | ⋮     |
| 31  | 32   | 33      |        |       |

She gives the last coin to **Corinne**.

**Method 2**

To find out who gets the last coin, look at the remainder (R) obtained when the number of coins is divided by 5 people.

If R = 0, the last coin goes to Ethel. If R = 1, the last coin goes to Ann. If R = 2, the last coin goes to Beth. If R = 3, the last coin goes to Corinne. If R = 4, the last coin goes to Denise.

$33 = 5 \times 6 + 3$
Remainder, R = 3

She gives the last coin to **Corinne**.

# Worked Example 2

Amos was paid $5 for each package that he delivered on time, and got $3 deducted for every late delivery. After delivering 30 packages, he was paid $102. How many packages did he deliver late?

If Amos delivered all 30 packages on time, his pay would be 30 × $5 = $150.

For every late delivery, Amos lost earnings of $5 for not delivering on time and had $3 deducted for being late, that is, he had a total of $5 + $3 = $8 deducted.

Total amount loss = $150 − $102
= $48

Number of packages delivered late = $48 ÷ $8
= 6

He delivered **6** packages late.

*Check:*
6 late deliveries and 30 − 6 = 24 timely deliveries
Total pay = 24 x $5 − 6 x $3 = $120 − $18 = $102 ✔

*Note:*
A common mistake is to simply do this:
$48 ÷ $3 = 16 ✗

**Answer all questions. Show your work and write your statements clearly.**

1. When Number $X$ is divided by Number $Y$, the quotient is 16 and the remainder is 3. The sum of the two numbers, the quotient, and the remainder is 345. What is Number $X$?

2. At the start of a trip, the odometer in Frank's car had a reading of 12,321, which is a palindromic number. After driving for 2 hours, the odometer showed another reading, which is also a palindromic number. If Frank was driving below a speed limit of 100 km/h, what was his speed?

A *palindromic number* reads the same forward and backward.

3. The product of the ages of two adults is 770. What is the sum of their ages?

Hint: Find the prime factorization of 770.

4. How many 3-digit numbers have a remainder of 7 when divided by 9, and a remainder of 2 when divided by 5?

Hint: Show that the smallest 3-digit number is 142.

5. At an election, a total of 240 votes were cast for four candidates. The winner won by a margin of 8, 13, and 15 votes over the other three candidates. What was the lowest number of votes received by a candidate?

6.  Two watches and one calculator cost $49 in all. Three watches and three calculators cost $99 in all. What is the cost of one watch?

    Hint: What is the cost of one watch and one calculator?

7.  Two bags and four hats cost $100 in all. Three bags and seven hats cost $164 in all. What is the cost of one hat?

    Hint: What is the cost of one bag and two hats?

8.  Three watches and five lamps cost $176 in all. Five watches and three lamps cost $208 in all. What is the cost of one lamp?

    Hint: What is the cost of eight watches and eight lamps?

9. Three calculators cost as much as seven mugs. Each calculator costs $12 more than each mug. What is the cost of one mug?

10. Three jackets cost as much as five shirts. Each shirt costs $16 less than each jacket. What is the cost of one shirt?

# 2 Fractions

## Worked Example 1

A balanced scale has a bag of sugar on its right pan. On its left pan, it has a bag of salt and a $\frac{2}{3}$-kg weight. The bag of salt is $\frac{2}{3}$ of the mass of the bag of sugar. What is the mass of the bag of sugar?

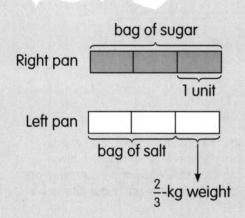

bag of sugar

Right pan

1 unit

Left pan

bag of salt

$\frac{2}{3}$-kg weight

1 unit $\longrightarrow \frac{2}{3}$ kg

3 units $\longrightarrow 3 \times \frac{2}{3}$ kg = 2 kg

The mass of the bag of sugar is **2 kg**.

# Worked Example 2

Richard spent $\frac{3}{4}$ of a sum of money and gave away $\frac{3}{4}$ of the remainder. He had $6 left. How much did he have at first?

## Method 1

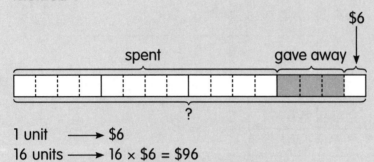

1 unit $\longrightarrow$ $6
16 units $\longrightarrow$ 16 × $6 = $96

He had **$96** at first.

Note: In drawing the model, we first divide the bar into 4 parts, 3 of which represent the amount spent. The remainder is then subdivided into 4 smaller equal parts. We go back to subdivide each of the 3 original parts into 4 smaller equal parts as well, thus dividing the entire bar into 16 parts.

## Method 2

$\frac{1}{4}$ of the remainder $\longrightarrow$ $6

$\frac{4}{4}$ of the remainder $\longrightarrow$ 4 × $6 = $24

Fraction left after spending = $1 - \frac{3}{4} = \frac{1}{4}$

$\frac{1}{4}$ of the sum of money $\longrightarrow$ $24

$\frac{4}{4}$ of the sum of money $\longrightarrow$ 4 × $24 = $96

He had **$96** at first.

# Practice Questions

**Answer all questions. Show your work and write your statements clearly.**

1. Lisa mixed $\frac{1}{2}$ kg of flour, $\frac{1}{3}$ kg of butter, and $\frac{1}{4}$ kg of sugar to make batter. What is the total mass of the batter?

2. A blue string is $23\frac{1}{4}$ cm long while a red string is $9\frac{2}{5}$ cm long. How much longer is the blue string than the red string?

3. The distance of a relay race was 3 km. Zoe ran $\frac{2}{5}$ of the distance. How many meters did she run?

4. Tommy has a rectangular strip of paper that is 21 cm long. If he cuts it into smaller pieces, each $2\frac{1}{3}$ cm long, how many pieces of paper will he have?

5. A balanced scale has a bag of flour on its right pan. On its left pan, it has a bag of rice and a 1-kg weight. The bag of rice is half the mass of the bag of flour. What is the mass of 2 similar bags of flour?

   Hint: Refer to Worked Example 2.

6. Sam spent $\frac{1}{2}$ of a sum of money on a book, and $\frac{1}{2}$ of the remainder on a bag of candy. He had $2 left. How much did he pay for the book?

   Hint: Draw a model diagram.

7.  Charles spent $\frac{1}{4}$ of his allowance on a shirt, and $\frac{2}{5}$ of the remainder on a book.
    (a)  What fraction of his allowance did he have left?
    (b)  If he spent $18 on the book, how much did he have at first?

    Hint: Draw a model diagram or use logical reasoning.

8.  A bag contains some red, blue, yellow, and green marbles. $\frac{3}{10}$ of the marbles are red, $\frac{2}{5}$ are green, and the rest are blue or yellow. There are twice as many blue marbles as yellow marbles. There are 17 fewer blue marbles than red marbles. How many marbles are there in all?

# Challenging Problems

## Worked Example 1

There is a total of 276 beads in Packet A and Packet B. There are 36 fewer beads in Packet B than $\frac{4}{9}$ of the number of beads in Packet A. How many beads are there in Packet A?

**Method 1**

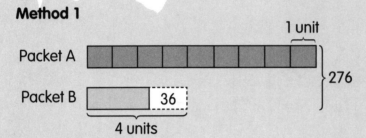

From the model,

13 units $\longrightarrow$ 276 + 36 = 312

1 unit $\longrightarrow$ 312 ÷ 13 = 24

9 units $\longrightarrow$ 9 × 24 = 216

There are **216** beads in Packet A.

**Method 2**

312

$\frac{4}{9}$A     A

$A + \frac{4}{9}A = 312$

$\frac{9}{9}A + \frac{4}{9}A = 312$

$\frac{13}{9}A = 312$

$A = 312 \times \frac{9}{13}$

$\quad = 216$

Packet A has **216** beads.

$A + B = 276$

$\frac{4}{9}A = B + 36$

$\frac{4}{9}A = (276 - A) + 36$

$\frac{4}{9}A = 312 - A$

# Worked Example 2

A ball is dropped onto the floor from a height of 128 cm. It rebounds to half of the height from where it was dropped, and this carries on for each subsequent rebound. How many centimeters has the ball covered by the time it hits the floor for the fourth time?

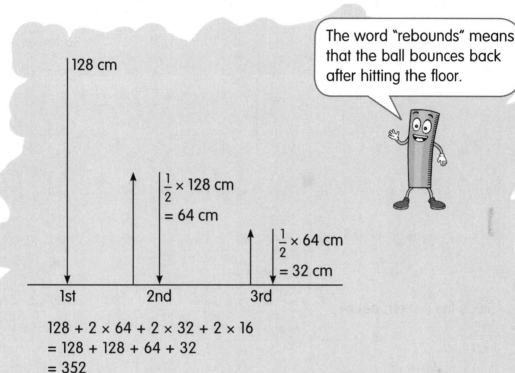

The word "rebounds" means that the ball bounces back after hitting the floor.

128 cm

$\frac{1}{2} \times 128$ cm
= 64 cm

$\frac{1}{2} \times 64$ cm
= 32 cm

1st      2nd      3rd

$128 + 2 \times 64 + 2 \times 32 + 2 \times 16$
$= 128 + 128 + 64 + 32$
$= 352$

The ball has covered **352 cm** by the time it hits the floor for the fourth time.

**Answer all questions. Show your work and write your statements clearly.**

1.  Without converting the fractions to decimals, state which of these fractions are smaller than $\frac{1}{5}$.

    A. $\frac{5}{21}$  B. $\frac{7}{36}$  C. $\frac{15}{72}$  D. $\frac{26}{101}$

2.  Study the pattern below.

    $$\frac{1}{1 \times 2} = \frac{1}{2}$$

    $$\frac{1}{1 \times 2} + \frac{1}{2 \times 3} = \frac{2}{3}$$

    $$\frac{1}{1 \times 2} + \frac{1}{2 \times 3} + \frac{1}{3 \times 4} = \frac{3}{4}$$

    $$\frac{1}{1 \times 2} + \frac{1}{2 \times 3} + \frac{1}{3 \times 4} + \frac{1}{4 \times 5} = \frac{4}{5}$$

    Given that $\frac{1}{1 \times 2} + \frac{1}{2 \times 3} + \frac{1}{3 \times 4} + \cdots + \frac{1}{2013 \times 2014} = \frac{x-2}{x-1}$, where $x$ is a whole number, find the value of $x$.

3. A fraction becomes $\frac{2}{3}$ when simplified. The product of its numerator and denominator is 216. What is the fraction?

   Hint: Express 216 as a product of prime factors or use guess and check.

4. Shirley had 52 more coins than Jim after Jim gave $\frac{1}{5}$ of his coins to her. If they had 260 coins in all, how many coins did Shirley have at first?

5. Ryan and Marie had some marbles. If Ryan lost 15 marbles, he would have 4 times as many marbles as Marie. If Ryan lost 75 marbles, he would have $1\frac{1}{2}$ times as many marbles as Marie. How many marbles did Ryan have at first?

6. Ruth and Bob have $130 in all. Ruth and Kevin have $115 in all. If Bob has $1\frac{1}{2}$ times as much money as Kevin, how much money does Ruth have?

7.  Larry and Steve have 171 marbles in all. The number of marbles Larry has is 39 fewer than $\frac{3}{7}$ of the number of marbles Steve has. How many marbles does Steve have?

8.  On Farm A, $\frac{4}{5}$ of the number of sheep are equal to $\frac{1}{2}$ of the number of sheep on Farm B. The total number of sheep on Farm A and Farm B is 845. How many sheep are there on Farm B?

9. Martha and Mary had 375 jelly beans in all. After Mary ate 24 jelly beans and Martha ate $\frac{1}{7}$ of her jelly beans, they each had the same number of jelly beans left. How many jelly beans did each girl have at first?

10. Adrian wants his lawn to be mown. 3 men apply for the task. The first man can mow the lawn in 6 hours; the second man can mow the lawn in 4 hours; and the third man can mow the lawn in 3 hours. How long will it take for the 3 men to complete the task if all of them mowed the lawn together?

# 3 Area and Perimeter

## Worked Example 1

The perimeter of a rectangle is 62 cm. Its length is 18 cm. What is its area?

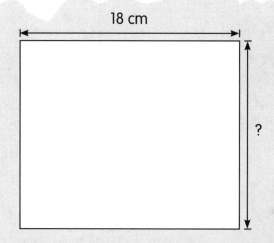

18 cm

?

Perimeter = 2 × (length + width)
         = 62 cm

Length + width = 62 cm ÷ 2
            = 31 cm

Width = 31 cm − 18 cm
      = 13 cm

Area = length × width
      = 18 cm × 13 cm
      = 234 cm$^2$

Its area is **234 cm$^2$**.

# Worked Example 2

Find the perimeter and area of the figure below.

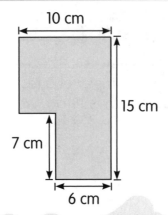

10 cm

15 cm

7 cm

6 cm

Perimeter = 2 × (10 cm + 15 cm)
          = 50 cm

Its perimeter is **50 cm**.

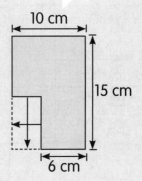

10 cm

15 cm

6 cm

We can use the following three methods to find the area of the figure.

**Method 1**

Area = (10 cm × 8 cm) + (7 cm × 6 cm)
      = 80 cm$^2$ + 42 cm$^2$
      = 122 cm$^2$

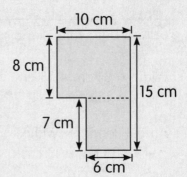

10 cm

8 cm

7 cm

15 cm

6 cm

## Method 2

Area = (8 cm × 4 cm) + (15 cm × 6 cm)
      = 32 cm² + 90 cm²
      = 122 cm²

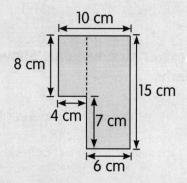

## Method 3

Area = (15 cm × 10 cm) − (7 cm × 4 cm)
      = 150 cm² − 28 cm²
      = 122 cm²

The area of the figure is **122 cm²**.

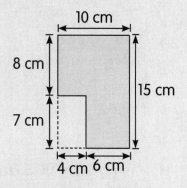

Which method do you prefer? Why?

What are the advantages and disadvantages of each method?

 **Practice Questions**

**Answer all questions. Show your work and write your statement clerly.**

1.  A rectangle has a perimeter of 78 cm. If its width is 17 cm, find its area.

    Hint: Refer to Worked Example 1.

2.  How many 3 cm by 5 cm rectangles can be cut from a 6 cm by 10 cm rectangle?

    Hint: Draw a diagram.

Challenge: Why do you think it is not advisable to solve without using a diagram, and simply do the calculation as follows: $\dfrac{6 \times 10}{3 \times 5} = \dfrac{60}{15} = 4$?

3. How many 10-cm square floor tiles are needed to cover a floor that measures 6 m by 8 m?

   Hint: Draw a diagram.

4. The perimeter of a square floor is 32 m. What is the cost of carpeting the floor at $8 per square meter?

5. A square and a rectangle have the same area. The rectangle has a length of 16 cm and a perimeter of 50 cm. What is the length of the square?

   Hint: What is the area of the rectangle?

6. Find the area of the figure on the right.

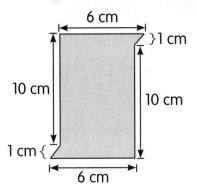

7. The figure on the right is made up of two identical overlapping rectangles. Each rectangle measures 25 cm by 8 cm. What is the area of the figure?

   Hint: Is there a region that is counted twice?

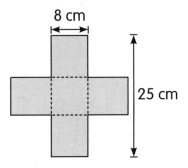

8. Gordon wants to plant trees along the sides of his rectangular plot of land measuring 55 m by 30 m. Each tree is planted 5 m away from the next tree. How many trees can he plant?

   Hint: Draw a diagram.

# Challenging Problems

## Worked Example 1

The figure shows a square made up of 6 rectangles. If the total perimeter of all 6 rectangles is 180 cm, find the area of the square.

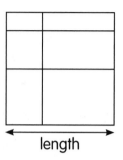

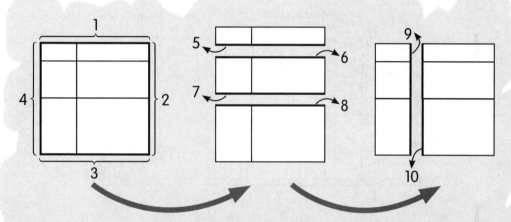

The illustrations above show 10 sides of the six rectangles.

Total perimeter of all rectangles = 10 × length of square

10 × length of square = 180 cm

Length of square = 180 cm ÷ 10
$\qquad$ = 18 cm

Area = 18 cm × 18 cm
$\quad$ = 324 cm$^2$

The area of the square is **324 cm$^2$**.

Note: You do not need to draw all the illustrations if you can figure out that the total perimeter represents 10 times the length of the square.

# Worked Example 2

A rectangular cardboard is 46 cm long and 27 cm wide. What is the maximum number of rectangles, each 7 cm long and 5 cm wide, that can be cut from it?

The diagram below shows that the maximum number of rectangles that can be cut out. There are 3 rows of 9 rectangles and 1 row of 6 rectangles, that is, a total of (9 × 3) + 6 = 33 rectangles.
It will leave a strip of width 1 cm on the right and at the bottom, and a 5 cm long and 3 cm wide rectangle.

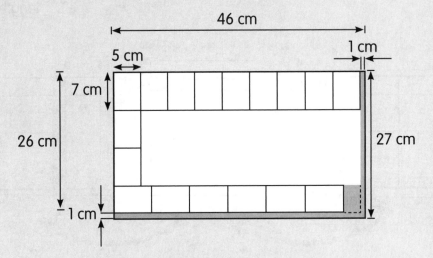

The maximum number of rectangles that can be cut from the rectangular cardboard is **33**.

Note: Without drawing a sketch or diagram, it is hard to determine the maximum number of rectangles that can be cut, such that a minimum amount of unused space is left.

**Answer all questions. Show your work and write your statements clearly.**

1. The length of a rectangle is 8 cm longer than its width. If its perimeter is 84 cm, what is its area?

2. The figure below is made up of 2 squares. Find its perimeter.

Hint: What is the length of each square?

3. Carol wants to cut rectangles of length 5 cm and width 3 cm from a piece of paper. The piece of paper measures 12 cm by 8 cm. What is the maximum number of rectangles that she can cut from it?

4. A rectangular cardboard is 50 cm long and 27 cm wide. What is the maximum number of rectangles, each of length 8 cm and width 6 cm, that can be cut from it?

5. A square of sides 12 cm is divided by 2 lines into rectangles with areas of 20 cm², 28 cm², 40 cm², and 56 cm². Where should the lines divide the square?

   Hint: Express the areas as a product of whole numbers, and look for any common factors.

6. The figure on the right is made up of 2 squares. The difference in their areas is 80 cm². If the sides of both squares are whole numbers, what is the perimeter of the figure?

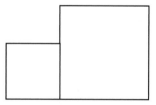

   Hint: Look for two square numbers that has a difference of 80.

7. Two rectangles have lengths of 13 cm and 19 cm respectively. Their total area is 376 cm². If both widths are whole numbers, what is the difference in their areas?

Hint: Look for multiples of 13 and 19 that sum up to 376.

8. The figure on the right is made of 4 identical rectangles. The length of each rectangle is twice its width. The area of the figure is 200 cm². Find its perimeter.

9. The figure below shows two overlapping squares. What is the area of the unshaded region?

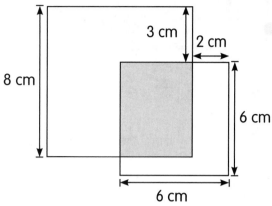

10. The figure below is made up of 13 identical rectangles. If its area is 520 cm², what is its perimeter?

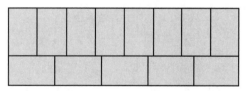

Hint: Express the width of a rectangle in terms of its length, or the length in terms of its width.

# 4 Area of Triangles

## Worked Example 1

Find the area of the symmetrical figure below.

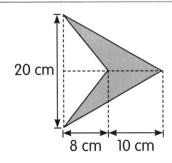

20 cm

8 cm | 10 cm

**Method 1**

Area of figure
= Area of triangle ABC
   – Area of triangle ADC

$= \frac{1}{2} \times AC \times BE - \frac{1}{2} \times AC \times DE$

$= \frac{1}{2} \times 20 \text{ cm} \times (10 \text{ cm} + 8 \text{ cm}) - \frac{1}{2} \times 20 \text{ cm} \times 8 \text{ cm}$

$= 180 \text{ cm}^2 - 80 \text{ cm}^2$

$= 100 \text{ cm}^2$

The area of the symmetrical figure is **100 cm²**.

**Method 2**

By symmetry, the area of triangle ABD is equal to the area of triangle CBD.

Area of figure $= 2 \times \left( \frac{1}{2} \times BD \times AE \right)$

$\qquad\qquad\quad = 2 \times \left( \frac{1}{2} \times 10 \text{ cm} \times 10 \text{ cm} \right)$

$\qquad\qquad\quad = 100 \text{ cm}^2$

The area of the symmetrical figure is **100 cm²**.

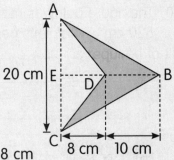

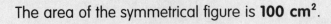

# Worked Example 2

What is the area of the shaded region in the figure below?

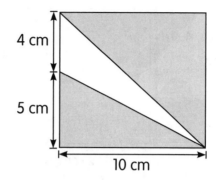

**Method 1**

Width of rectangle = 4 cm + 5 cm
$\qquad\qquad\qquad$ = 9 cm

Area of rectangle = 9 cm × 10 cm
$\qquad\qquad\qquad$ = 90 cm$^2$

Area of unshaded triangle = $\dfrac{1}{2}$ × base × height

$\qquad\qquad\qquad\qquad\qquad$ = $\dfrac{1}{2}$ × 4 cm × 10 cm

$\qquad\qquad\qquad\qquad\qquad$ = 20 cm$^2$

Area of shaded region = 90 cm$^2$ − 20 cm$^2$
$\qquad\qquad\qquad\qquad$ = 70 cm$^2$

The area of the shaded region is **70 cm²**.

**Method 2**

The shaded region can be divided into 2 triangles, A and B.

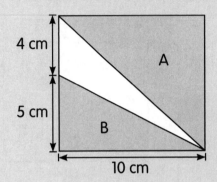

Area of Triangle A $= \frac{1}{2} \times 10$ cm $\times 9$ cm

$\qquad\qquad\qquad = 45$ cm$^2$


Area of Triangle B $= \frac{1}{2} \times 10$ cm $\times 5$ cm

$\qquad\qquad\qquad = 25$ cm$^2$


Area of shaded region $= 45$ cm$^2 + 25$ cm$^2$

$\qquad\qquad\qquad\qquad = 70$ cm$^2$

The area of the shaded region is **70 cm$^2$**.

# Worked Example 3

What is the area of the shaded region of the figure?

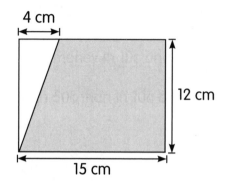

## Method 1

Area of shaded region = Area of rectangle − Area of triangle

$$= (15 \text{ cm} \times 12 \text{ cm}) - \left(\frac{1}{2} \times 4 \text{ cm} \times 12 \text{ cm}\right)$$
$$= 180 \text{ cm}^2 - 24 \text{ cm}^2$$
$$= 156 \text{ cm}^2$$

The area of the shaded region is **156 cm²**.

## Method 2

Form a new rectangle by creating another identical shaded region.

Area of shaded region

$$= \frac{1}{2} \times \text{area of the new rectangle}$$

$$= \frac{1}{2} \times (15 \text{ cm} + 11 \text{ cm}) \times 12 \text{ cm}$$

$$= 156 \text{ cm}^2$$

The area of the shaded region is **156 cm²**.

### Method 3

Divide the shaded region into 2 triangles, A and B.

Area of shaded region
= Area of Triangle A + Area of Triangle B
$$= \left(\frac{1}{2} \times 12 \text{ cm} \times 11 \text{ cm}\right) + \left(\frac{1}{2} \times 15 \text{ cm} \times 12 \text{ cm}\right)$$
$$= 66 \text{ cm}^2 + 90 \text{ cm}^2$$
$$= 156 \text{ cm}^2$$

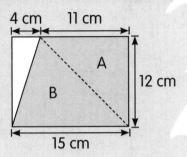

The area of the shaded region is **156 cm²**.

### Method 4

Divide the shaded region into 2 triangles, P and Q.

Area of shaded region
= Area of Triangle P + Area of Triangle Q
$$= \left(\frac{1}{2} \times 11 \text{ cm} \times 12 \text{ cm}\right) + \left(\frac{1}{2} \times 15 \text{ cm} \times 12 \text{ cm}\right)$$
$$= 66 \text{ cm}^2 + 90 \text{ cm}^2$$
$$= 156 \text{ cm}^2$$

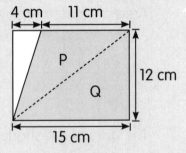

The area of the shaded region is **156 cm²**.

Solving a problem using different methods enhances one's creative thinking!

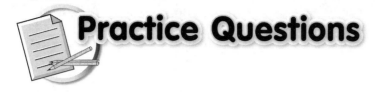

# Practice Questions

**Answer all questions. Show your work and write your statements clearly.**

1. The perimeter of the triangle below is 30 cm. What is its area?

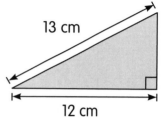

13 cm

12 cm

Hint: What is the length of the third side of the triangle?

2. Keith is given some triangles, as shown below. He needs to paste the triangles on a piece of paper of length 6 cm and width 4 cm. What is the maximum number of triangles that he can paste onto the paper without overlapping?

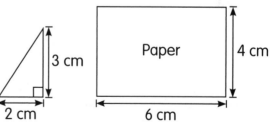

3 cm

2 cm

Paper

4 cm

6 cm

3. In the figure on the right, BD is parallel to AE. Triangles ABE, ACE, and ADE have the same area. Explain why.

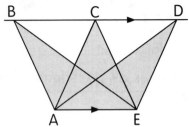

4. The figure on the right is symmetrical. What is its area?

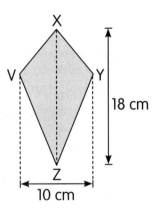

Hint: Refer to Worked Example 1.

5. ABCD is a square of sides 17 cm. What is the area of the unshaded region?

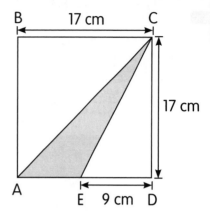

6. In the figure on the right, ABCD is a square of sides 12 cm. E is the midpoint of BC and F is the midpoint of CD. What is the area of triangle AEF?

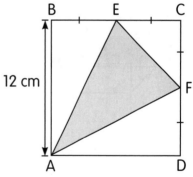

7. What is the area of the shaded region of the figure on the right?

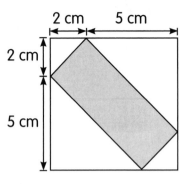

Challenge: Find the area of the shaded region in more than one way.

8. The figure on the right is made up of a rectangle and a triangle. What is the perimeter and the area of the figure?

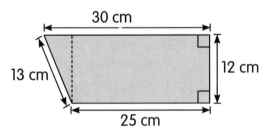

Challenge: Try different ways of solving the question.

## Worked Example 1

In the figure below, the length of square ABCG is 8 cm. The length of square GDEF is 12 cm. What is the area of the unshaded region?

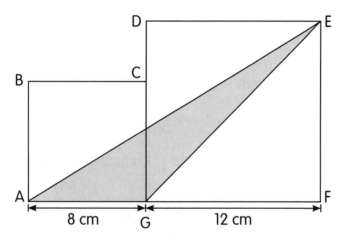

Area of triangle AEG = $\frac{1}{2}$ × 8 cm × 12 cm

$\qquad\qquad\qquad\quad$ = 48 cm$^2$

Area of unshaded region
= Area of square ABCG + Area of square GDEF − Area of triangle AEG
= (8 cm × 8 cm) + (12 cm × 12 cm) − 48 cm$^2$
= 64 cm$^2$ + 144 cm$^2$ − 48 cm$^2$
= 160 cm$^2$

The area of the unshaded region is **160 cm$^2$**.

# Worked Example 2

The length of square A is 8 cm. The length of square B is 6 cm. Squares A and B overlap each other. What is the difference in the areas of the two unshaded regions?

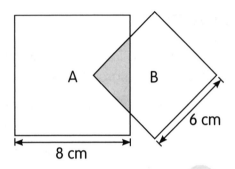

**Case 1:**

If Squares A and B do not overlap each other, the difference in areas
= (8 cm × 8 cm) − (6 cm × 6 cm)
= 64 cm² − 36 cm²
= 28 cm²

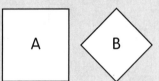

**Case 2:**

If Square B is inside Square A, the difference in areas
= (8 cm × 8 cm) − (6 cm × 6 cm)
= 64 cm² − 36 cm²
= 28 cm²

**Case 3:**

If half of Square B overlaps Square A, the difference in areas
$$= \left(8 \text{ cm} \times 8 \text{ cm} - \frac{1}{2} \times 6 \text{ cm} \times 6 \text{ cm}\right) - \left(\frac{1}{2} \times 6 \text{ cm} \times 6 \text{ cm}\right)$$
= (64 cm² − 18 cm²) − 18 cm²
= 28 cm²

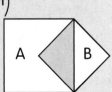

The above three cases show that regardless of how the squares are overlapped, the difference in the areas of the two unshaded regions is always **28 cm²**.

**Answer all questions. Show your work and write your statements clearly.**

1.  The length of square ABCG is 8 cm. The length of square GDEF is 6 cm. What is the area of the shaded region?

    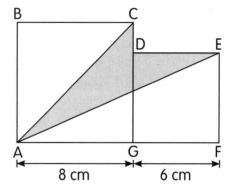

    Hint: Refer to Worked Example 1.

2.  The diagonal of the square below is 10 cm. Find its area.

    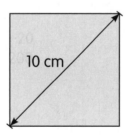

    Hint: Rearrange the square to be a triangle.

3. The figure on the right is formed by overlapping two identical squares. The overlapping area is $\frac{1}{4}$ of the area of each square. What fraction of the figure is shaded?

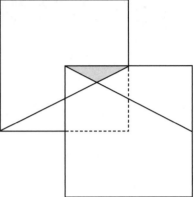

4. The figure on the right shows a square puzzle made up of seven shapes. If the area of the square puzzle is 1 m², what is the area of each shape?

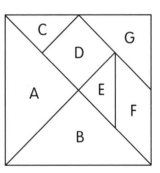

Hint: Construct dotted lines and see how the shapes are related to each other.

5.  The figure on the right shows two equilateral triangles: ABD and CDE. AB is parallel to EC. The height of equilateral triangle CDE is $\frac{1}{4}$ of the height of equilateral triangle ABD. What fraction of the equilateral triangle ABD is shaded?

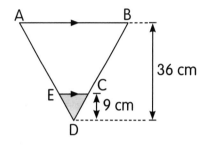

6.  In the figure on the right, AJ = JI = IH = HG, and BC = CD = DE = EF. What fraction of the figure is shaded?

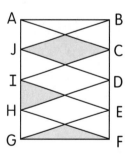

7. The length of square PQUV is 10 cm. The length of square RSTU is 6 cm. Find the area of the shaded region.

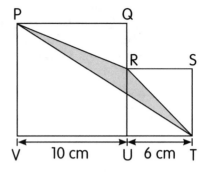

Hint: Refer to Worked Example 1.

8. Rectangle ABCD is divided into four triangles. Triangle AED has an area of 16 cm², triangle DEC has an area of 25 cm², and triangle EBC has an area of 24 cm². Find the area of triangle ABE.

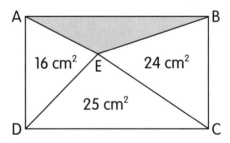

9. PQRS is a square of sides 24 cm. If PX = $\frac{1}{3}$ XS and QY = $\frac{1}{4}$ QR, what is the area of the shaded region?

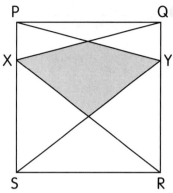

Hint: Separate the shaded region into two triangles.

10. In the figure below, the lines AC and BD meet at O. If OA = 50 cm, OB = 40 cm, OC = 60 cm, and OD = 48 cm, find the

value of $\dfrac{\text{Area of } \triangle OAB}{\text{Area of } \triangle OCD}$.

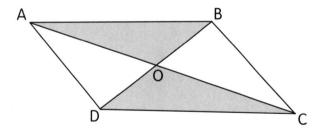

11. In the figure below, the lines PR and QS meet at point O. If PO = 4 cm, QO = 5 cm, RO = 6 cm, and SO = 7.5 cm, find the value

of $\dfrac{\text{Area of } \triangle POS}{\text{Area of } \triangle QOR}$.

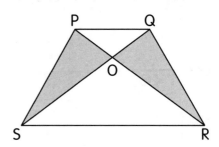

# 5 Ratio

## Worked Example 1

> The ratio of the number of Joel's stickers to the number of Tony's stickers is 3 : 5. Joel has 36 stickers. How many stickers does Tony have?

**Method 1**

```
              36
        ┌───────────┐
Joel    │   │   │   │
        └───────────┘

Tony    │ │ │ │ │ │
        └───────────┘
              ?
```

From the model,
3 units ⟶ 36
1 unit  ⟶ 36 ÷ 3 = 12
5 units ⟶ 5 × 12 = 60

Tony has **60** stickers.

**Method 2**

Joel's stickers : Tony's stickers

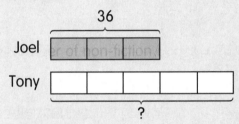

× 12     3 : 5     × 12

36 : 60

Tony has **60** stickers.

# Worked Example 2

The ratio of the number of boys to the number of girls in a class is 5 : 3. There are 8 more boys than girls. How many students are there in the class?

**Method 1**

Boys

Girls

?

8

From the model,

2 units ⟶ 8

1 unit ⟶ $8 \div 2 = 4$

8 units ⟶ $8 \times 4 = 32$

There are **32** students in the class.

**Method 2**

| Boys | : | Girls | : | Total |
|------|---|-------|---|-------|
| 5 | : | 3 | : | $5 + 3 = 8$ |

$$\frac{5}{8} - \frac{3}{8} = \frac{2}{8}$$

$\frac{2}{8}$ of the class represents 8 students.

$\frac{8}{8}$ of the class represents $8 \times \frac{8}{2} = 32$ students.

There are **32** students in the class.

# Worked Example 3

The ratio of the number of Cindy's stickers to the number of Roy's stickers is 4 : 7. If Cindy gives $\frac{1}{8}$ of her stickers to Roy, what will be the new ratio of the number of Cindy's stickers to the number of Roy's stickers?

**Method 1**

Cindy's stickers : Roy's stickers

           4 : 7

           8 : 14

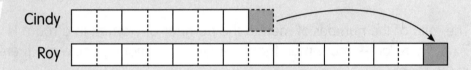

The new ratio of the number of Cindy's stickers to the number of Roy's stickers is **7 : 15**.

**Method 2**

Cindy's stickers : Roy's stickers

           4 : 7

           8 : 14

     8 − 1 : 14 + 1

           7 : 15

The new ratio of the number of Cindy's stickers to the number of Roy's stickers is **7 : 15**.

# Practice Questions

**Answer all questions. Show your work and write your statements clearly.**

1.  The ratio of the number of Kate's marbles to the number of Peter's marbles is 5 : 6. Peter has 24 marbles. How many marbles does Kate have?

    Hint: Refer to Worked Example 1.

2.  The ratio of the number of men to the number of women in a room is 7 : 4. There are 9 more men than women. How many people are there in the room?

    Hint: Refer to Worked Example 2.

3.  A students' club has 60 members. The ratio of the number of boys to the number of girls is 7 : 5. How many more boys than girls are there in the club?

4.  The ratio of the number of Mike's envelopes to the number of Doris's envelopes is 3 : 7. If Mike gives $\frac{1}{6}$ of his envelopes to Doris, what will be the new ratio of the number of Mike's envelopes to the number of Doris's envelopes?

    Hint: Refer to Worked Example 3.

5.  The ratio of the number of Esther's cards to the number of Andy's cards is 5 : 8. If Esther gives $\frac{3}{10}$ of her cards to Andy, what will be the new ratio of the number of Esther's cards to the number of Andy's cards?

    Hint: Refer to Worked Example 3.

6.  The ratio of the number of Daniel's coins to the number of Mary's coins is 9 : 13. If Mary has 52 coins, how many coins do they have altogether?

7.  Mark bought some oranges, pineapples, and apples. The ratio of the mass of the oranges to the mass of the pineapples was 4 : 7. The mass of the apples was $\frac{5}{11}$ of the total mass of the fruits. The pineapples weighed 18 kg more than the oranges. What was the total mass of the fruits?

8.  The ratio of the ages of Jay, Tim, and Angela now is 3 : 7 : 9. 10 years ago, Tim was 25 years old. What will be the ratio of their ages in 5 years' time?

9.  Joyce had $75 and Leslie had $48. After each spent the same amount of money, the ratio of the amount of money Joyce had to the amount of money Leslie had was 7 : 4. How much did each of them have left?

# Challenging Problems

## Worked Example 1

The ratio of Ann's money to Jean's money was 4 : 7. After Ann spent half of her money and Jean spent $45, Jean had twice as much money as Ann. How much money did Ann have at first?

**Method 1**

Before

Ann

Jean

After                                    $45

Ann

Jean

3 units ⟶ $45
1 unit ⟶ $45 ÷ 3 = $15
4 units ⟶ 4 × $15 = $60

Ann had **$60** at first.

**Method 2**

Ann's money : Jean's money

$$4 \quad : \quad 7$$
$$4 - 2 \quad : \quad 7 - 3$$
$$2 \quad : \quad 4$$

3 units ⟶ $45
1 unit ⟶ $45 ÷ 3 = $15
4 units ⟶ 4 × $15 = $60

Ann had **$60** at first.

# Worked Example 2

Gary had some 50¢ and $1 coins. The ratio of the number of 50¢ coins to the number of $1 coins was 2 : 3. After Gary received more 50¢ and $1 coins from his father, the ratio became 1 : 3. The total value of his 50¢ coins in the end was $10. How many $1 coins did Gary receive from his father if he had eighteen 50¢ coins at first?

50¢ coins : $1 coins

$\times 9 \overset{2}{\underset{18}{\huge(}} : \overset{3}{\underset{27}{\huge)}} \times 9$

Gary had twenty-seven $1 coins at first.

$10 = 1,000¢
1,000¢ ÷ 50¢ = 20

Gary has twenty 50¢ coins now.

50¢ coins : $1 coins

$\times 20 \overset{1}{\underset{20}{\huge(}} : \overset{3}{\underset{60}{\huge)}} \times 20$

Gary has sixty $1 coins now.

60 − 27 = 33

Gary received **thirty-three** $1 coins from his father.

**Answer all questions. Show your work and write your statements clearly.**

1.  The ratio of the amount of money Terry had to the amount of money Maria had was 4 : 9. Then Terry spent half of his money and Maria spent $20. Maria now has twice as much money as Terry. How much money did Terry have at first?

    Hint: Refer to Worked Example 1.

2.  The ratio of the number of Michael's books to the number of Janet's books was 4 : 5. Michael received another 24 books. He now has twice as many books as Janet. How many books did Michael have at first?

3.  The ratio of the number of Adrian's crayons to the number of Susan's crayons was 3 : 5. Susan gave 21 crayons to her cousin, Peter. She now has half as many crayons as Adrian. How many crayons did Adrian have at first?

4.  The ratio of the amount of money Elaine had to the amount of money Lynn had was 5 : 9. Elaine spent half of her money and Lynn spent $15. Lynn now has three times as much money as Elaine. How much money did Elaine have at first?

5. In a school, the ratio of the number of boys to the number of girls is $8 : 5$. One quarter of the boys and $\frac{1}{15}$ of the girls wear glasses. When another 48 students who wear glasses join the school, the total number of students who wear glasses in the school becomes 216. How many boys wore glasses at first?

6. The ratio of the number of Joe's marbles to the number of Fred's marbles was $8 : 3$. After Joe gave 15 marbles to Fred, they each had the same number of marbles. How many marbles did Joe have at first?

7.  The ratio of the number of men to the number of women registered for a marathon was 17 : 15. 90 fewer men and 80 fewer women turned up for the marathon. The ratio of the number of men to the number of women became 8 : 7. How many people registered for the marathon?

8.  In a school, the ratio of the number of boys to the number of girls is 2 : 3 and the ratio of the number of girls to the number of teachers is 7 : 4. What is the ratio of the number of students to the number of teachers?

    Hint: Convert each ratio to an equivalent ratio such that the new value for the numbers of girls is common for both ratios.

9.  The ratio of the number of David's cards to the number of Tom's cards is 4 : 5. The ratio of the number of Tom's cards to the number of Jack's cards is 7 : 8. If Jack has 24 more cards than David, how many cards does Tom have?

    Hint: Convert each ratio to an equivalent ratio such that the new value for Tom is common for both ratios.

10. Five gold coins can be balanced by a weight. Four silver coins can also balance the same weight. How many silver coins with twenty gold coins are required to balance ten similar weights?

## Worked Example 1

Without performing any calculation, explain why (a) and (b) will have the same answer.
(a)  0.12)5.6          (b)  12)560

### Method 1

When we shift the decimal points of 0.12 and 5.6 two places to the right, we multiply the numbers by 100.

$$5.6 \div 0.12 = (5.6 \times 100) \div (0.12 \times 100)$$
$$= 560 \div 12$$

Therefore, (a) and (b) will have the same answer.

### Method 2

Interpret 5.6 ÷ 0.12 as "How many groups of $0.12 can you get from $5.60?"

If we convert dollars to cents, the question becomes "How many groups of 12 cents can you get from 560 cents", which we can solve by dividing 560 by 12.

Therefore, (a) and (b) will have the same answer.

# Worked Example 2

Emily bought 32.8 m of cloth to make 6 shirts and 2 pairs of pants. She used 3.25 m of cloth for each shirt and the remaining cloth for the pants. How much cloth did she use for each pair of pants?

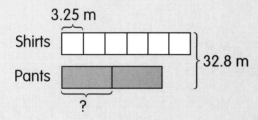

Length of cloth to make 6 shirts = 6 × 3.25 m
= 19.5 m

Length of cloth to make 2 pairs of pants
= 32.8 m − 19.5 m
= 13.3 m

Length of cloth to make 1 pair of pants
= 13.3 m ÷ 2
= 6.65 m

She used **6.65 m** of cloth for each pair of pants.

# Worked Example 3

2 wallets and 4 caps cost $67.90.
5 wallets and 9 caps cost $160.25.
What is the cost of 1 cap?

$67.90

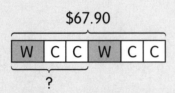

| W | C | C | W | C | C |

?

2 wallets + 4 caps = $67.90
1 wallet + 2 caps  = $67.90 ÷ 2
                   = $33.95

$160.25

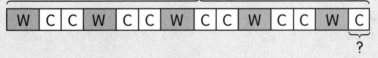

| W | C | C | W | C | C | W | C | C | W | C | C | W | C |

?

5 wallets + 10 caps = 5 × $33.95
                    = $169.75
5 wallets + 9 caps  = $160.25 (given)
            1 cap   = $169.75 − $160.25
                    = $9.50

The cost of 1 cap is **$9.50**.

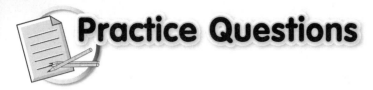

# Practice Questions

**Answer all questions. Show your work and write your statements clearly.**

1. Given that $4.85 \times 3.24 = 15.714$, find the value of the following:
   (a)  $157.14 \div 0.00324$
   (b)  $0.015714 \div 485$
   (c)  $0.0324 \times 4{,}850$

2. James mixed 0.125 L of Syrup A with 0.375 L of Syrup B and 0.25 L of Syrup C. What was the volume of the mixture?

3.  Ryan bought a portable hard drive for $74.95 and a thumb drive for $23.50. He gave the cashier a $100 bill. How much change did he receive?

4.  Arthur bought 7 pens for $1.32 each. He gave the cashier a $20 bill. How much change did he receive?

5.  A bottle holds 6 ounces of cough syrup. If May needs to drink 0.4 ounces of cough syrup each day, in how many days will she finish it?

6. If a bunch of grapes costs $1.35 per kg, what fraction of a kilogram of grapes can you buy with $0.45?

7. Mr. Charles bought 8 notebooks, 8 files, 8 watches, and 9 balls. How much did he spend altogether?

| Item | Cost |
|---|---|
| Notebook | $2.45 |
| File | $4.25 |
| Ball | $12.50 |
| Watch | $14.95 |

8. The difference between Alex's and Cathy's height is the same as the difference between Cathy's and Denise's height. Alex is 1.52 m tall and Cathy is 1.23 m tall. If Denise is shorter than Cathy, find Denise's height.

9. Roger had $1,200. He bought a cell phone with 0.4 of the money and a helmet with 0.5 of the remaining money. What was the amount of money Roger had left?

10. Laurel and Harry worked 5 hours each. They earned $120 in all. If Laurel earned $0.60 more than Harry per hour, how much did Laurel earn per hour?

11. Bag A contained three times the mass of sand in Bag B. After 6.25 kg of sand were removed from Bag A and 1.4 kg were removed from Bag B, Bag B contained 0.35 kg more sand than Bag A. What was the new mass of sand in Bag B?

   Hint: Draw a model diagram.

# Challenging Problems

## Worked Example 1

In the recurring decimal 0.123451234512345…, what is the 2,018th digit to the right of the decimal point?

A *recurring decimal* has a sequence of digits that is repeated.

Notice that the pattern of 5 digits, 12345, repeats itself in the decimal.

When a pattern of 5 digits repeats itself in the decimal, we say that the decimal has a period of 5.

$$2{,}018 \div 5 = 403 \text{ R } 3 \qquad \text{or} \qquad \begin{aligned} 2{,}018 &= 5 \times 403 + 3 \\ &= 2{,}015 + 3 \end{aligned}$$

Since 2,018 is 3 more than 2,015, which is a multiple of 5, the 2,018th digit will be the 3rd digit to the right of 5. The 2,018th digit is **3**.

# Worked Example 2

Two calculators and four batteries cost $33. Three calculators and two batteries cost $40.50. What is the cost of one battery?

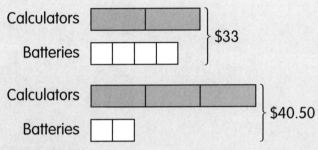

## Method 1

Cost of 6 calculators and 4 batteries = $40.50 × 2

= $81

Cost of 4 calculators = $81 − $33

= $48

Cost of 2 calculators = $48 ÷ 2

= $24

Cost of 4 batteries = $33 − $24

= $9

Cost of 1 battery = $9 ÷ 4

= $2.25

The cost of one battery is **$2.25**.

## Method 2

Cost of 1 calculator and 2 batteries = $33 ÷ 2

= $16.50

Cost of 2 calculators = $40.50 − $16.50

= $24

Cost of 4 batteries = $33 − $24

= $9

Cost of 1 battery = $9 ÷ 4

= $2.25

The cost of one battery is **$2.25**.

**Answer all questions. Show your work and write your statements clearly.**

1.  Jeffrey multiplies a number by itself and then adds 10. His answer is 23.69. What is the number?

    Hint: Work backwards.

2.  In the recurring decimal 0.05341053410…, what is the 50th digit to the right of the decimal point?

    Hint: Refer to Worked Example 1.

3.  When the fraction $\frac{3}{7}$ is expressed in decimal form, which digit is in the 21st decimal place?

    Hint: Look for a pattern.

4.  Anita has $42.55 worth of coins in her piggy bank. The coins are in denominations of 5¢, 10¢, 20¢, 50¢, and $1. If there are an equal number of coins for each denomination, how many coins are there in all?

5.  Sam bought 15 pies and 7 slices of cake for $55.25. If each pie cost $\frac{2}{5}$ as much as a slice of cake, what was the total cost of 1 pie and 2 slices of cake?

6.  The total mass of Robbie and a trophy is 69.95 kg. The total mass of Sarah and the same trophy is 63.1 kg. If Robbie and Sarah have a mass of 116.05 kg in all, find the mass of
    (a)  the trophy,
    (b)  Robbie,
    (c)  Sarah.

7.  The volume of water in Tank B was 3 times the volume of water in Tank A. After Hilda poured 0.45 L of water into Tank A and another 12.75 L of water into Tank B, the volume of water in Tank B became 5 times the volume of water in Tank A. What was the initial volume of water in Tank B?

8. Alvin saved a portion of his daily pocket money. Each day, he saved $1.40 more than the previous day. At the end of one week, he had saved $36.40. How much did he save on the third day?

9. Paul and Ian had a total of $63. After Paul gave 0.3 of his money to Ian, Ian gave $\frac{1}{3}$ of his total amount of money to Calvin. If all three boys had the same amount of money in the end, how much did Paul have at first?

   Hint: Use a suitable number of units to represent Paul's money. How many units does $63 represent?

10. A transport company delivered 78 plates to a shop. It charged $1.50 for every plate delivered. It had to compensate $9.50 for every broken plate. If the company collected $73 from a shop owner, how many plates were broken?

Hint: For every broken plate, the transport company loses $11.

11. A whole number, N, lies between 35 and 45. When N is multiplied by 0.45, the product is another whole number. Find the value of N.

Hint: Express 0.45 as a fraction in its lowest term.

# 7 Volume

## Worked Example 1

A total of 24 unit cubes are used to form a rectangular prism. How many different rectangular prisms can be formed using all 24 unit cubes?

The factors of 24 are 1, 2, 3, 4, 6, 8, 12, and 24.

Look for three factors with a product of 24.

The possible dimensions of the rectangular prism could be:

$1 \times 1 \times 24$
$1 \times 2 \times 12$
$1 \times 3 \times 8$
$1 \times 4 \times 6$
$2 \times 2 \times 6$
$2 \times 4 \times 3$

**Six** different rectangular prisms can be formed.

Note: $2 \times 4 \times 3$ is equivalent to $2 \times 3 \times 4$.

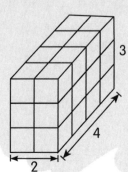

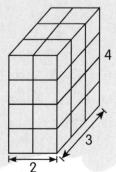

# Worked Example 2

Pitcher A contained the same volume of water as Pitcher B. After 445 mL of water was poured out from Pitcher A and 65 mL of water was poured out from Pitcher B, the volume of water in Pitcher B was 5 times the volume of water in Pitcher A. What was the volume of water in each pitcher at first?

445 mL

Pitcher A

Pitcher B

65 mL

4 units ⟶ 445 mL – 65 mL = 380 mL

1 unit ⟶ 380 mL ÷ 4 = 95 mL

95 mL + 445 mL = 540 mL

The volume of water in each pitcher at first was **540 mL**.

# Practice Questions

**Answer all questions. Show your work and write your statements clearly.**

1.  The rectangular prism below has a volume of $\frac{1}{4}$ m³. What is its length?

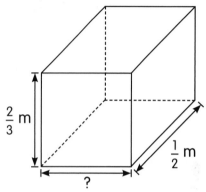

2.  The width of a rectangular block is 16 cm. It is half as wide as its length. The width is 4 times its height. What is the volume of the block?

3. A tank, measuring 22 m by 18 m by 12 m, is filled with water to a depth of 7 m. When more water is added to the tank, the height of the water level becomes 10.8 m. How much water is added?

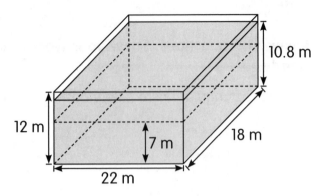

4. The figure below shows a tank. How much more water is required to fill the tank completely? Give your answer in liters and milliliters.
   (1 L = 1,000 cm³)

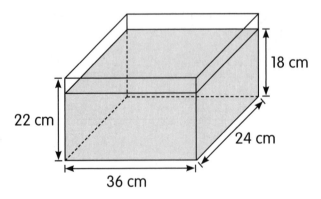

5. A container, measuring 38 cm by 30 cm by 18 cm, is $\frac{3}{5}$-filled with water. How much more water is required to fill the tank completely? Give your answer in liters and milliliters. (1 L = 1,000 cm³)

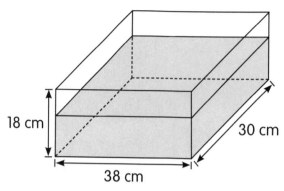

Hint: What capacity of the container is not filled with water?

6. A wooden block measures 48 cm by 36 cm by 28 cm. A 4-cm cube is cut away from each of its corners. What is the volume of the remaining block?

Hint: How many 4-cm cubes will be cut off?

7. A tank, measuring 60 cm by 55 cm by 35 cm, was filled with water to its brim. 29.7 L of the water is poured out from the tank. What is the new height of the water?

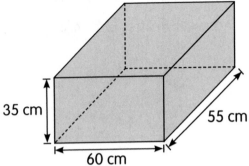

35 cm

55 cm

60 cm

8. A piece of square cardboard measures 10 cm by 10 cm. A box can be formed by cutting out identical squares from each corner and folding up the sides. Find the volume of the box formed when
   (a) 1-cm squares are cut out,
   (b) 2-cm squares are cut out,
   (c) 3-cm squares are cut out.

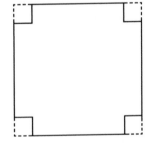

9. The total capacity of three tanks P, Q, and R is 522 L. The capacity of Tank P is 30 L more than Tank Q. The capacity of Tank R is 4 times as much as the capacity of Tank Q. Find the capacity of Tank P.

Hint: Draw a model diagram.

10. In the figure below, the container is filled with water to a depth of 10 cm. What is the volume of water?

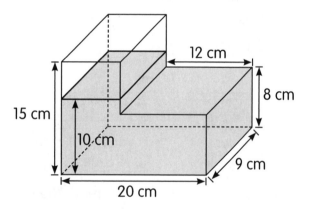

# Challenging Problems

## Worked Example 1

When 6 identical cubes were placed in a measuring beaker containing some water, the total volume of the water and the cubes was 850 mL. When 2 cubes were removed, the total volume decreased to 700 mL. What was the volume of the water in the beaker?

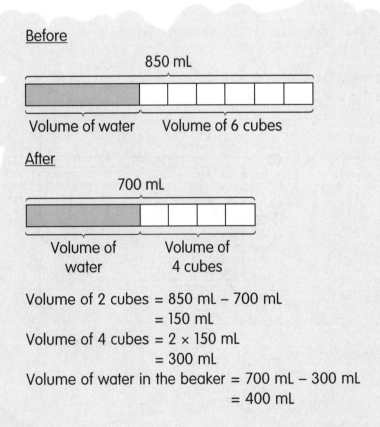

Before

850 mL

Volume of water    Volume of 6 cubes

After

700 mL

Volume of          Volume of
water              4 cubes

Volume of 2 cubes = 850 mL – 700 mL
                  = 150 mL
Volume of 4 cubes = 2 × 150 mL
                  = 300 mL
Volume of water in the beaker = 700 mL – 300 mL
                              = 400 mL

The volume of the water in the beaker was **400 mL**.

Note: This question may be solved without model drawing. However, a model
      does help us to visualize the problem better.

# Worked Example 2

A tank, measuring 60 cm by 40 cm by 30 cm, was half-filled with water. The water from the tank is poured out to fill 20 identical jars, each of capacity 750 cm³. What is the height of the water level left in the tank?

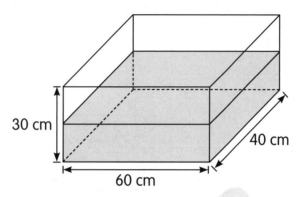

## Method 1

Height of water in the tank = 30 cm ÷ 2
= 15 cm
Volume of water in the tank = 60 cm × 40 cm × 15 cm
= 36,000 cm³
Total volume of water required to fill 20 jars = 20 × 750 cm³
= 15,000 cm³
Volume of water left in the tank = 36,000 cm³ − 15,000 cm³
= 21,000 cm³
Height of the water level left in the tank = $\dfrac{21{,}000 \text{ cm}^3}{60 \text{ cm} \times 40 \text{ cm}}$

= **8.75 cm**
The height of the water level left in the tank is **8.75 cm**.

## Method 2
Height of water in the tank = 30 cm ÷ 2
= 15 cm
Volume of water that is poured out = 20 × 750 cm³
Height of the decrease in water level = $\dfrac{20 \times 750}{60 \times 40}$
= 6.25 cm

Height of water level left in the tank = 15 cm − 6.25 cm = **8.75 cm**
The height of the water level left in the tank is **8.75 cm**.

**Answer all questions. Show your work and write your statements clearly.**

1. A tank, which measures 20 cm by 16 cm by 12 cm, was $\frac{2}{3}$-filled with water. A stone of volume 240 cm$^3$ is placed in the tank. What is the new height of the water level in the tank?

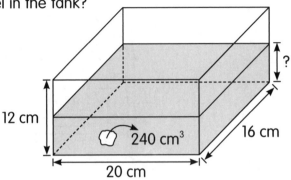

Hint: What is the increase in height of water level when the stone was placed into the tank?

2. The ratio of the volume of water in Container P to the volume of water in Container Q was 5 : 3. After 46 mL of water was poured out from Container P and 120 mL of water was poured into Container Q, both containers had the same volume of water. What was the volume of water in Container P at first?

3.  The figure below shows a tank which was $\frac{1}{3}$-filled with water. 50 L of water was then added to fill the tank to its brim. What was the height of the water level in the tank at first?

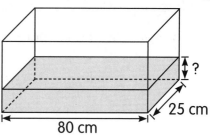

?

25 cm

80 cm

4.  The figure below shows a tank which is $\frac{4}{5}$ filled with water. After 30 L of water were poured out of the tank, it became $\frac{2}{3}$-full. What was the height of the water level in the tank at first?

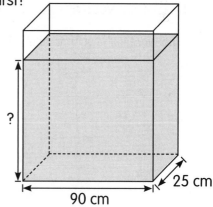

?

25 cm

90 cm

5.  A tank, measuring 120 cm by 100 cm by 80 cm, was half filled with water. When 6 identical pails of water were poured into the tank, it became $\frac{4}{5}$-filled. If each pail was filled with water to its brim, what is the capacity of each pail? Give your answer in milliliters.

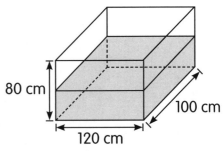

Hint: The capacity of each pail is equivalent to the volume of water it can hold when filled to its brim.

6.  A container of capacity 5,500 mL contained 2,145 mL of water. A 7-cm metal cube was placed in it. How much more water could the container hold? Give your answer in liters and milliliters.

Hint: What is the volume of the 7-cm metal cube?

7. A two-liter pitcher contained 764 cm³ of water. When 12 identical metal cubes were placed into the pitcher, 264 cm³ of water overflowed. What was the length of each metal cube?

Hint:

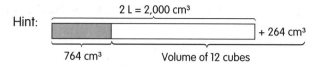

8. Joyce used $\frac{3}{5}$ of the water in a container to fill 4 glasses and 7 cups.

If the capacity of each glass was twice that of a cup, how many cups could she fill with the remaining water in the container?

Hint: How many cups can be filled by $\frac{3}{5}$ of the water in the container?

9. Twelve bottles of water can fill $\frac{5}{8}$ of a container. To fill the container completely, another six bottles and five glasses of water are needed. How many glasses of water have the same capacity as the container?

10. What is the maximum number of rectangular blocks, each measuring 7 cm by 5 cm by 3 cm, that can be placed inside a rectangular box measuring 14 cm by 15 cm by 16 cm?

Hint: Consider any possible unused space.

# 8 Percentage

## Worked Example 1

Jenny and Sylvia have 320 stamps in all. The number of Jenny's stamps is equal to 60% of Sylvia's stamps. How many stamps does Sylvia have?

### Method 1

| Sylvia | | | | | | | | | | |

Sylvia | Jenny bar model } 320

Sylvia's stamps ⟶ 10 units
Jenny's stamps ⟶ 6 units (60% of 10 units)

16 units ⟶ 320
1 unit ⟶ $320 \div 16 = 20$
10 units ⟶ $10 \times 20 = 200$

Sylvia has **200** stamps.

### Method 2

$60\% = \frac{60}{100} = \frac{3}{5}$

Jenny's stamps $= \frac{3}{5} \times$ Sylvia's stamps

Jenny's stamps + Sylvia's stamps = 320

$\frac{3}{5} \times$ Sylvia's stamps $+ \frac{5}{5} \times$ Sylvia's stamps $= 320$

$\frac{8}{5} \times$ Sylvia's stamps $= 320$

Sylvia's stamps $= 320 \times \frac{5}{8}$

$= 200$

Sylvia has **200** stamps.

# Worked Example 2

Pearlyn has 10% more stickers than David. If Pearlyn gives 24 stickers to David, David will have 10% more stickers than Pearlyn. How many stickers do Pearlyn and David have in all?

**Method 1**

<u>Before</u>                                              10%

Pearlyn

David

<u>After</u>                                                24

Pearlyn

David

                                                        10%

1 unit ⟶ 24

21 units ⟶ 21 × 24 = 504

Pearlyn and David have **504** stickers in all.

**Method 2**

                    David    Pearlyn
+ 24 stickers ⌐   100%      110%  ⌐ – 24 stickers
               ↳   110%      100%  ↵

10% ⟶ 24

210% ⟶ $\frac{24}{10}$ × 210 = 504

Pearlyn and David have **504** stickers in all.

# Worked Example 3

There are 60 members in a music club. 25% of them like jazz music, 15% of them like pop music, 20% of them like rock music, and 50% of the rest like classical music. How many members enjoy classical music?

Percentage of members who like jazz, pop, and rock music
= 25% + 15% + 20%
= 60%

Percentage of members who enjoy other types of music
= 100% − 60%
= 40%

Percentage of members who enjoy classical music
= 50% of 40%

$= \dfrac{1}{2} \times 40\%$

= 20%

Number of members who enjoy classical music
= 20% of 60

$= \dfrac{1}{5} \times 60$

= 12

**12** members enjoy classical music.

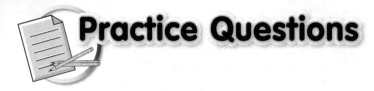

# Practice Questions

**Answer all questions. Show your work and write your statements clearly.**

1. A total of 48 students sat for a math exam. Only 75% of them passed. How many students passed the exam?

2. During an election, Albert received 60% of the 30 votes cast. Anthony received the remaining votes. How many more votes did Albert receive?

3. A shop owner sold 10 cell phones and made a total profit of 20%. What was his percentage profit for each phone?

4. Samuel bought a watch at a discount of 30%. If he had paid $119, what was the original price of the watch?

5. There are some mint chocolates and dark chocolates in a box. The number of mint chocolates is 25% of the number of dark chocolates. What percentage of the chocolates is mint?

6. What is the percentage of the number of whole numbers, from 4 to 23, which are multiples of 5?

   Hint: The number of whole numbers from 4 to 23 is not 23 − 4 = 19.

7.  A total of 50 boys and 30 girls participated in a contest. 20% of the boys and 30% of the girls received prizes. What percentage of the contestants received prizes?

    Hint: How many boys and how many girls received prizes?

8.  Tim wanted to sell his watch at a discount of 10%. However, he then decided to increase the discounted price by 5%. What was the new percentage discount?

9.  Serene and Derek have 270 stickers in all. Serene has 25% more stickers than Derek. How many stickers does Derek have?

 **Challenging Problems**

## Worked Example 1

There were 300 books on a shelf. 30% of the books were fiction and the rest were non-fiction. When another 120 books were added, the percentage of non-fiction books increased to 75%. How many fiction books were added to the shelf?

<u>Before</u>
Number of fiction books = 30% × 300
$\qquad\qquad$ = 90

Number of non-fiction books = 70% × 300 $\qquad$ or $\qquad$ 300 − 90
$\qquad\qquad$ = 210 $\qquad\qquad\qquad\qquad$ = 210

<u>After adding 120 books</u>
Total number of fiction and non-fiction books = 300 + 120
$\qquad\qquad$ = 420
Number of non-fiction books = 75% × 420
$\qquad\qquad$ = 315

Number of non-fiction books added = 315 − 210
$\qquad\qquad$ = 105

Number of fiction books added = 120 − 105
$\qquad\qquad$ = 15
**15** fiction books were added to the shelf.

Note: We may also present the given information using a table.

|  | Fiction | Non-fiction |
|---|---|---|
| **Before** |  |  |
| **After** |  |  |

# Worked Example 2

The length of a rectangle is increased by 25%. Its width is decreased by 25%. What is the percentage change in its area?

**Method 1**

New length of rectangle = 125% × length
$\qquad\qquad\qquad\qquad$ = 1.25 length

New width of rectangle = 75% × width
$\qquad\qquad\qquad\qquad$ = 0.75 width

New area of rectangle = (1.25 length) × (0.75 width)
$\qquad\qquad\qquad\qquad$ = (1.25 × 0.75) area
$\qquad\qquad\qquad\qquad$ = 0.9375 area

New area expressed as percentage = 0.9375 × 100%
$\qquad\qquad\qquad\qquad\qquad\qquad\qquad$ = 93.75%

Percentage change in area = 100% − 93.75%
$\qquad\qquad\qquad\qquad\qquad$ = 6.25%

The percentage change in its area is **6.25%**.

**Method 2**

Since both the length and the width are not given, we can assign them some suitable values.

| | Length | Width | Area |
|---|---|---|---|
| **Before** | 100 ⟍ + 25% | 60 ⟍ − 25% | 100 × 60 = 6,000 |
| **After** | 125 ⟋ | 45 ⟋ | 125 × 45 = 5,625 |

Percentage decrease in area = $\dfrac{6{,}000 - 5{,}625}{6{,}000} \times 100\%$

$\qquad\qquad\qquad\qquad\qquad\qquad$ = 6.25%

The percentage change in its area is **6.25%**.

**Answer all questions. Show your work and write your statements clearly.**

1. Jonathan sold two television sets for $6,000 each. He made a profit of 20% on the first set and had a loss of 20% on the second set. How much total profit or loss did he have?

2. If the length and width of a rectangle are increased by 20%, what is the percentage increase in its area?

3. If a square's length and width are increased by 30%, find the percentage increase in its area.

4.  Jack and Jill each had the same amount of money. After six months, Jack's money increased by 10% and Jill's money decreased by 10%. A year later, Jack's money decreased by 10% and Jill's money increased by 10%. Who had more money in the end?

5.  At a fruit stall, 30% of the fruits are oranges, 40% are apples, and the rest are pineapples. If 20% of the oranges and 30% of the apples are rotten, what percentage of the fruits are in good condition?

    Hint: Assign a suitable value to be the number of fruits.

6. Melvin has 30% more marbles than Henry. If Melvin gives 30 marbles to Henry, both of them would have the same number of marbles. How many marbles does Henry have?

7. Bobby takes 66 candies from a jar and Mike takes the remaining candies. If Bobby gives 24 candies to Mike, the number of candies Mike has would increase by 60%. How many candies must Bobby give to Mike so that they will have the same number of candies?

Hint: What percentage of Mike's candies represents the 24 candies?

8. Dave had 400 old Singapore and Malaysia coins. 60% of the coins were Singapore coins. After buying more Singapore coins, the percentage of Malaysia coins decreased to 32%. How many Singapore coins did he buy?

   Hint: The number of Malaysia coins remained the same; only its percentage had changed.

9. There were 400 stamps in an album. 35% of them were Indonesia stamps and the rest were Malaysia stamps. When 100 more stamps were added, the percentage of Malaysia stamps increased to 70%. How many Indonesia stamps were added to the album?

   Hint: What was the new total number of Malaysia stamps?

10. If 25% of Number A is 125 and 0.35% of Number B is 10.5, what is the sum of numbers A and B?

# 9 Angles and Triangles

## Worked Example 1

In the figure below, the measure of $\angle x$ is twice the measure of $\angle y$. Find the measures of $\angle x$ and $\angle y$.

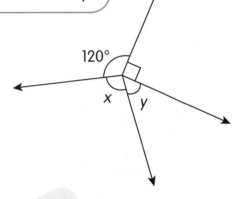

Since the sum of angles at a point is 360°,

$$m\angle x + m\angle y + 90° + 120° = 360°$$
$$m\angle x + m\angle y = 360° - 90° - 120°$$
$$= 150°$$

Since $m\angle x = 2\ m\angle y$,

$$2(m\angle y) + m\angle y = 150°$$
$$3\ \angle y = 150°$$
$$m\angle y = 150° \div 3$$
$$= 50°$$

$$m\angle x = 2 \times 50°$$
$$= 100°$$

Hence, $m\angle x = \mathbf{100°}$ and $m\angle y = \mathbf{50°}$.

# Worked Example 2

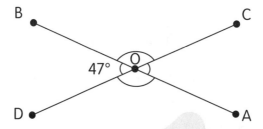
In the figure below, AB and CD are straight line segments. Find the measures of ∠AOC, ∠AOD and ∠BOC.

B                 C

47°   O

D                 A

**Method 1**

Since ∠AOC and ∠BOD are vertically opposite angles,
m∠AOC = 47°

Since ∠AOD and ∠BOD are angles on a straight line segment,
m∠AOD = 180° − 47°
        = 133°

Since ∠AOD and ∠BOC are vertically opposite angles,
m∠BOC = 133°

Hence, m∠AOC = **47°**, m∠AOD = **133°**, and m∠BOC = **133°**.

**Method 2**

Since ∠DOB and ∠BOC are angles on a straight line segment,
m∠BOC = 180° − 47°
        = 133°

Since ∠AOD and ∠BOC are vertically opposite angles,
m∠AOD = 133°

Since ∠AOD, ∠DOB, ∠BOC, and ∠AOC are angles at a point,
m∠AOC = 360° − 133° − 47° − 133°
        = 47°

Hence, m∠AOC = **47°**, m∠AOD = **133°**, and m∠BOC = **133°**.

# Worked Example 3

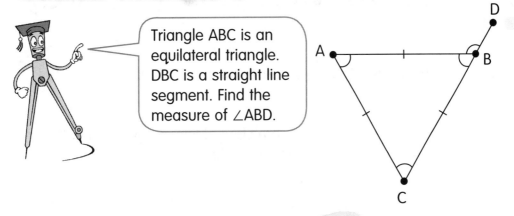

Triangle ABC is an equilateral triangle. DBC is a straight line segment. Find the measure of ∠ABD.

An equilateral triangle has 3 equal angles. Each interior angle is 60°. Hence, m∠A = m∠B = m∠C = 60°.

Since ∠CBA and ∠ABD are angles on a straight line segment,
m∠ABD = 180° − 60°
      = 120°

Hence, m∠ABD = **120°**.

# Worked Example 4

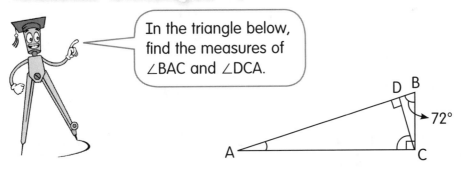

In the triangle below, find the measures of ∠BAC and ∠DCA.

In △ABC, m∠BAC = 180° − 90° − 72°
               = 18°

In △ACD, m∠DCA = 180° − 18° − 90°
               = 72°

Hence, m∠BAC = **18°** and m∠DCA = **72°**.

# Practice Questions

**Answer all questions. Show your work and write your statments clearly.**

1. In the figure below, PQ and RS are straight line segments. Find the measures of ∠x and ∠y in the figure below.

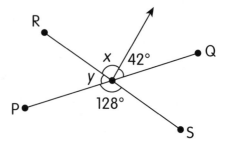

2. In the figure on the right, find the measure of ∠x.

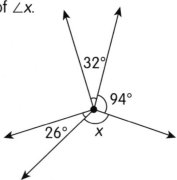

3. In the figure on the right, RS, PQ, and TU are straight line segments. Find the measure of ∠x.

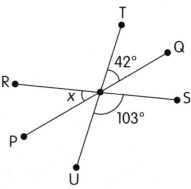

4. In the figure on the right, XY is a straight line segment. What is the measure of $\angle z$?

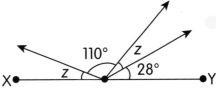

5. In the figure on the right, what is the measure of $\angle q$?

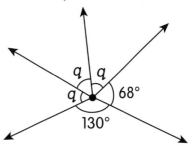

6. In the figure on the right, the measure of $\angle x$ is five times the measure of $\angle y$. What are the measures of $\angle x$ and of $\angle y$?

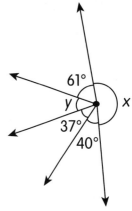

7. In triangle PQR, PQ = RQ and m∠RQP = 76°. Find the measures of ∠QPR and ∠PRQ.

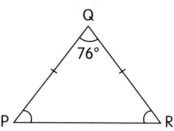

8. In the figure on the right, ABC is an equilateral triangle and AE = AD. Find the measure of ∠ADE.

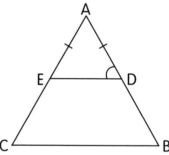

9. In triangle PQR, PR = QR. Find the measure of ∠PQS.

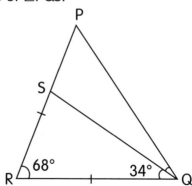

10. In the figure on the right, AB is a straight line segment. Find the measure of ∠p.

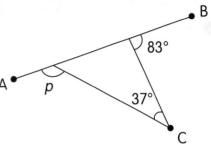

11. Triangle ABC is an isosceles triangle and CA = CB. Find the measure of ∠x.

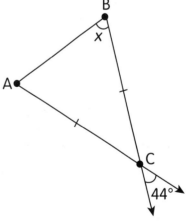

# Challenging Problems

## Worked Example 1

In the figure below, the ratio of the measure of ∠AOB to the measure of ∠AOD is 2 : 3. Find the measure of ∠AOD.

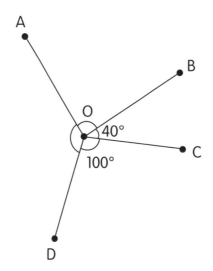

**Method 1**

m∠AOB : m∠AOD

    2 : 3

m∠AOB + m∠AOD = 2 units + 3 units
$$= 5 \text{ units}$$

5 units  ⟶  360° − 100° − 40° = 220°
1 unit   ⟶  220° ÷ 5 = 44°
3 units  ⟶  3 × 44° = 132°

The measure of ∠AOD is **132°**.

**Method 2**

m∠AOB : m∠AOD = 2 : 3

m∠AOB + m∠AOD + 40° + 100°
= 360° (∠ sum of a point)

$m\angle AOD + \dfrac{2}{3} m\angle AOD$

= 360° − 100° − 40° = 220°

$\dfrac{5}{3} m\angle AOD = 220°$

$m\angle AOD = 220° \times \dfrac{3}{5}$

$$= 44° \times 3$$
$$= 132°$$

The measure of ∠AOD is **132°**

**Answer all questions. Show your work and write your statements clearly.**

1. In the figure on the right, PRT and PQT are isosceles triangles. If RQ is a straight line segment, find the measures of $\angle a$ and $\angle b$.

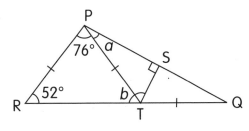

2. In the figure on the right, QT is a straight line segment, PRQ is a right-angled triangle and STR is an equilateral triangle. Find the measure of $\angle z$.

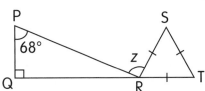

3. In the figure on the right, PQRS is a square. Find the measure of ∠a.

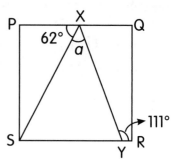

Hint: Note that SX is not equal to YX.

4. In the figure on the right, PAY is an isosceles triangle and AB is a straight line segment. Find the measure of ∠YAP.

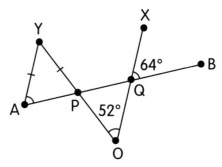

Hint: Show that m∠YAP = m∠QPO.

5. The figure is made up of two triangles, XYZ and XVW. Triangle XYZ is an isosceles triangle and XY = XZ. Find the measure of ∠p.

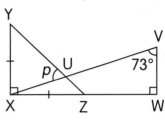

6. Triangle PQR is an isosceles triangle. Triangle QSR is an equilateral triangle. Find the measure of ∠y.

Hint: ∠y = ∠PRQ − ∠SRQ

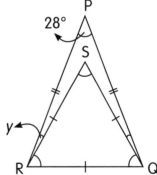

7. The figure is made up of two triangles, PQT and PST. ∠PTR = 17° and ∠RPQ = 32°. If triangle PST is an isosceles triangle, find the measure of ∠y.

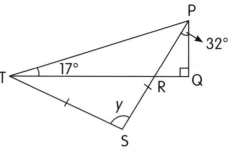

8. What is the sum of the six unknown marked angles?

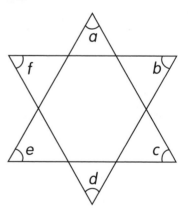

Hint: Notice that the figure is made up of two intersecting triangles.

# 10 Quadrilaterals

## Worked Example 1

In the figure below, ABCD is a trapezoid, triangle ADE is an isosceles triangle and ED = EA. Find the measure of $\angle x$.

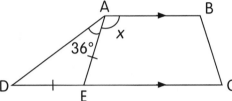

Since triangle ADE is an isosceles triangle,
$m\angle EAD = m\angle EDA = 36°$

$m\angle AED = 180° - 36° - 36°$
$\qquad = 108°$

$m\angle AEC = 180° - 108°$
$\qquad = 72°$

Alternatively, since the exterior angle of a triangle is equal to the sum of the interior opposite angles,
$m\angle AEC = 36° + 36°$
$\qquad\quad = 72°$

Since each pair of angles between two parallel sides adds up to 180°,
$m\angle x = 180° - 72°$
$\qquad = 108°$

Hence, $m\angle x = \mathbf{108°}$.

# Worked Example 2

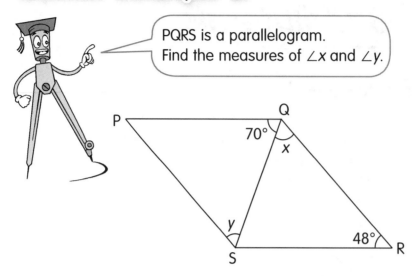

PQRS is a parallelogram.
Find the measures of ∠x and ∠y.

Since each pair of angles between two parallel sides add up to 180°,

70° + m∠x + 48° = 180°

$$m\angle x = 180° - 70° - 48°$$
$$= 62°$$

Since the opposite angles of a parallelogram are equal, m∠SPQ = 48°.

$$m\angle y = 180° - m\angle PQS - m\angle SPQ \qquad (\angle \text{ sum of a } \Delta)$$
$$= 180° - 70° - 48°$$
$$= 62°$$

Hence, m∠x = **62°** and m∠y = **62°**.

*Note*: Each pair of angles between two parallel sides adds up to 180°. An equivalent statement is:

The sum of the interior angles of parallel lines is 180°.

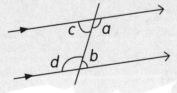

m∠a + m∠b = 180°
m∠c + m∠d = 180°

# Worked Example 3

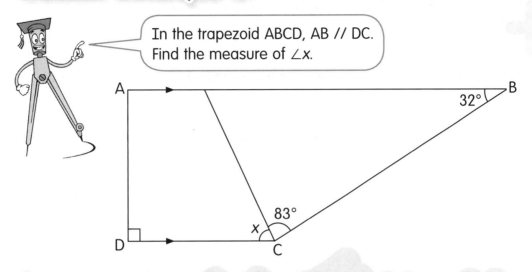

In the trapezoid ABCD, AB // DC. Find the measure of ∠x.

## Method 1

Since each pair of angles between two parallel line segments adds up to 180°, m∠ABC + m∠BCD = 180°.

m∠BCD = 180° − 32°
= 148°

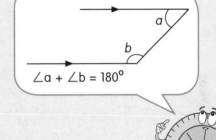

∠a + ∠b = 180°

m∠x + 83° = 148°
m∠x = 148° − 83°
= 65°

Hence, m∠x = 65°.

## Method 2

In △BCE, m∠BEC = 180° − 83° − 32°
= 65°

m∠AEC = 180° − 65°
= 115°

m∠x = 180° − m∠AEC
= 180° − 115°
= 65°

Hence, m∠x = **65°**.

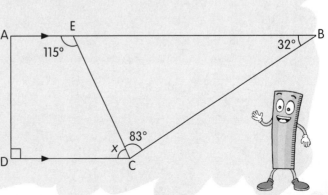

**Answer all questions. Show your work and write your statements clearly.**

1. In the figure on the right, ABCD is a parallelogram. Find the measure of ∠p.

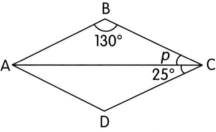

2. In the figure on the right, ABCD is a parallelogram. Find the measure of ∠CBD.

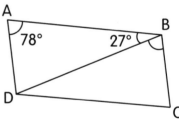

3. In the figure on the right, PQRS is a parallelogram. Find the measure of ∠y.

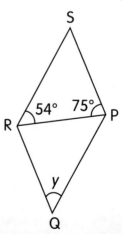

4. In the figure on the right, PQRS is a parallelogram. Find the measure of ∠SQR.

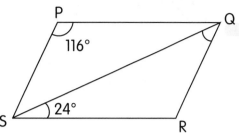

5. Find the measures of the unknown angles in the parallelogram ABCD.

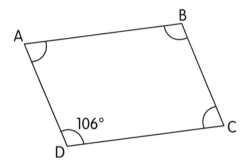

6. A rhombus is a special type of parallelogram. Find the measures of the unknown angles in the rhombus ABCD.

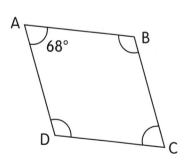

7.  In the figure on the right, EFGH is a rhombus. Find the measure of ∠x.

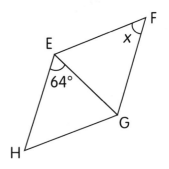

8.  In trapezoid PQRS, PQ // SR. Find the measure of ∠PST.

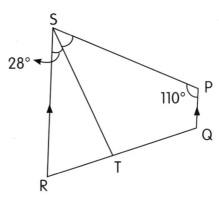

9. In the figure on the right, PQST is a parallelogram, QRS is an isosceles triangle, PR is a straight line segment and RQ = RS. Find the measures of ∠x and ∠y.

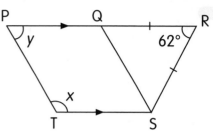

10. In trapezoid ABCD, AB // DC, ADE is an isosceles triangle, and EA = ED. Find the measure of ∠ADC.

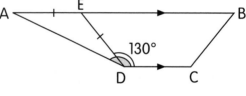

# Challenging Problems

## Worked Example 1

In square ABCD, DBE is a straight line segment and AE = CE. If m∠AEC = 70°, find the measure of ∠x.

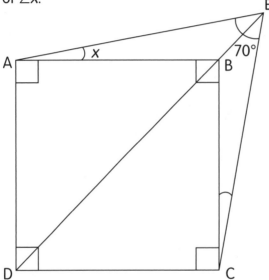

Since AE = CE, A and C are the vertices of the square ABCD, triangle ACE is an isosceles triangle.

m∠AEC = 70°

m∠CAE = m∠ECA

    = (180° − 70°) ÷ 2

    = 55°

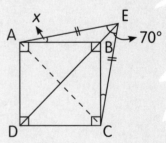

Since CA is the diagonal of square ABCD,
m∠CAB = 45°

m∠x = 55° − 45°

    = **10°**

Hence, m∠x = **10°**.

**Answer all questions. Show your work and write your statements clearly.**

1. In the figure on the right, EFGI is a trapezoid, EFHI is a parallelogram and FGH is an isosceles triangle, where HG = HF. Find the measure of ∠FGH.

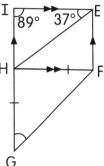

   Hint: Not all given angles are needed to find the unknown angle.

2. In rectangle KLMN, PLM is an isosceles triangle, LP = LM, and ∠KNP = 28°. Find the measure of ∠NPM.

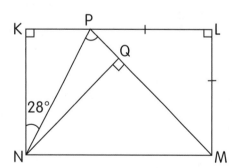

   Hint: Find the measures of ∠KPN and ∠LPM.

3. In the figure on the right, PQR is an isosceles triangle, where RP = RQ and PQRS is a trapezoid. Find the measure of ∠SRQ.

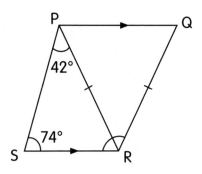

4. In the figure on the right, ABCE is a rectangle. Find the measure of ∠EBD.

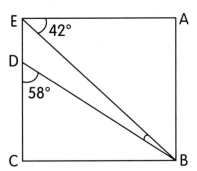

Hint: m∠ABC = 90°

5. PQRS and QRTU are parallelograms. Find the measure of ∠PQS.

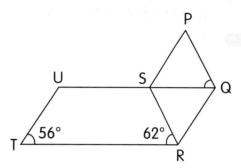

Hint: Look for interior angles of parallel line segments.

6. In rectangle PQRS, ADB is a straight line segment, SA = SB, and BRC is an equilateral triangle. Find the measure of ∠ABC.

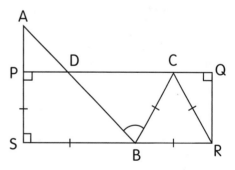

Hint: Find the measures of ∠ABS and ∠CBR.

7. In trapezoid PQRS, PQ // SR, and PR and SQ are straight line segments. If PQ = PS, find the measure of ∠QTR.

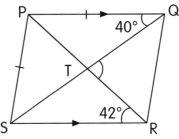

Hint: m∠QTR = m∠TSR + m∠TRS

8. In the figure on the right, PQRS is a parallelogram and ABCD is a rectangle. If m∠APB = 105° and m∠DCR = 38°, find the measure of ∠CBQ.

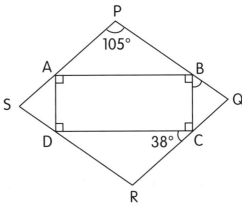

Hint: How are m∠SPQ and m∠RQP related?

9.  In the figure on the right, ABCD is a parallelogram, and BCE is an isosceles triangle. Find the measures of ∠BAE and ∠BEA.

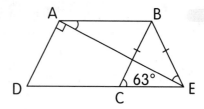

Hint: How are m∠BAD and m∠BCD related?

10. In the figure on the right, ABCD is a square, and BEC is an equilateral triangle. If ABE and CDE are isosceles triangles, where BA = BE and CE = CD, find the measure of ∠x.

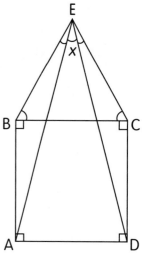

Hint: m∠BEA + m∠x + m∠CED = 60°

# 11 Average and Plots

## Worked Example 1

The average income of Adam, Irene, and Fiona is $560. Irene earns twice as much as Adam. Fiona earns twice as much as Irene. How much does Fiona earn?

Adam
Irene
Fiona
$3 \times \$560$

From the model,

7 units $\longrightarrow$ $3 \times \$560 = \$1,680$
1 unit $\longrightarrow$ $\$1,680 \div 7 = \$240$
4 units $\longrightarrow$ $4 \times \$240 = \$960$

Fiona earns **$960**.

# Worked Example 2

The average of six numbers is 6. If 3 is subtracted from four of the numbers, what is the new average?

**Method 1**

Since the average of six numbers is 6, then the total sum of the six numbers is $6 \times 6 = 36$.

If 3 is subtracted from four of the numbers, we subtract $4 \times 3 = 12$ from the sum.

New sum = 36 – 12
         = 24

New average = 24 ÷ 6
            = 4

The new average is **4**.

**Method 2**

The total sum subtracted is $3 \times 4 = 12$.

Suppose the six numbers were each 6. Subtracting 12 is equivalent to subtracting 2 from each of the six numbers: $12 \div 6 = 2$.

6    6    6    6    6    6

| – 2   | – 2   | – 2   | – 2   | – 2   | – 2

4    4    4    4    4    4

So, the new average is **4**.

# Worked Example 3

Use the information below to answer the questions.

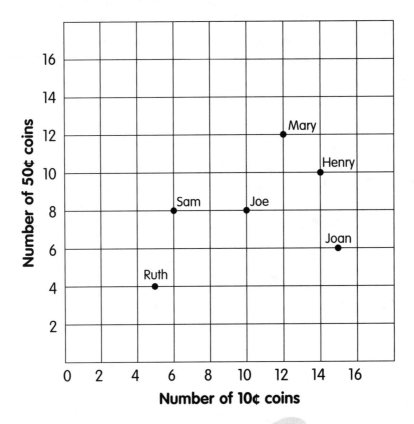

(a) Who has two more 10¢ than 50¢ coins?

10 − 8 = 2

**Joe** has two more 10¢ than 50¢ coins.

(b) Who has $4.60 in 10¢ and 50¢ coins?

6 × 10¢ = 60¢

8 × 50¢ = 400¢ = $4

60¢ + $4 = $4.60

**Sam** has $4.60 in 10¢ and 50¢ coins.

(c) Who has the same number of 10¢ and 50¢ coins?

Mary has twelve 10¢ coins and twelve 50¢ coins.

**Mary** has the same number of 10¢ and 50¢ coins.

(d) Who has twice as much money in 10¢ and 50¢ of another?

|  | Number of 10¢ coins | Number of 50¢ coins |
|---|---|---|
| Joe | 10 | 8 |
| Ruth | 5 | 4 |

**Joe** has twice as much money in 10¢ and 50¢ as **Ruth**.

(e) Who has $1.50 more in 50¢ than in 10¢ coins?
15 × 10¢ = 150¢
          = $1.50
6 × 50¢ = 300¢
          = $3
$3 − $1.50 = $1.50

**Joan** has $1.50 more in 50¢ than in 10¢ coins.

(f) Which two people have a total amount of $11?
Sam:
6 × 10¢ = 60¢
8 × 50¢ = 400¢
          = $4
$4 + 60¢ = $4.60

Henry:
14 × 10¢ = 140¢
          = $1.40
10 × 50¢ = 500¢
          = $5
$5 + $1.40 = $6.40

$4.60 + $6.40 = $ 11

**Sam** and **Henry** have a total amount of $11.

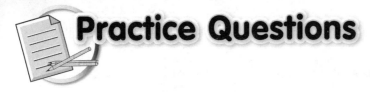

# Practice Questions

**Answer all questions. Show your work and write your statements clearly**

1.  The digits 2, 3, and 7 can form six different 3-digit numbers. Find the average of these six numbers.

2.  Lynette's average score on five tests is 18. If she scores 24 points on her sixth test, what is her average score on all six tests?

3.  Robin received an average score of 64 points on his first three tests. On his fourth test, he scored 28 more points than the average score on his first three tests. What is his new average score?

4. The average of five numbers is 7. If one of the five numbers is removed, the average of the four remaining numbers is 6. What is the value of the number that was removed?

5. The average test score of Sean and Ted is 68 points. The average test score of Sean, Ted, and Mary is 72 points. What is Mary's test score?

6. On a test, the average score of 25 boys and 15 girls is 68 points. The average score of the boys is 62 points. What is the average score of the girls?

7. There are 100 black paper clips, 150 white paper clips, and 250 silver paper clips in a box. The average mass of the paper clips is 3.9 g.
   (a) Find the total mass of the paper clips.
   (b) If the box of paper clips has a mass of 2,596 g, what is the mass of the empty box?

8. Eugene's average score of three tests is 85 points. If he wants his average score to increase by 2 points, what score must he get for the fourth test?

9. The total mass of eight tennis players is 645 kg and the average mass of seven baseball players is 90 kg. What is the average mass of all the players?

10. Bill read 61 pages of a book on the first day, 49 pages on the second day, and 52 pages on the third day. On the fourth day, he read 6 more pages than the average number of pages he had read on the first three days. How many pages did he read on the fourth day?

11. Study the information in the graph below to answer the questions.

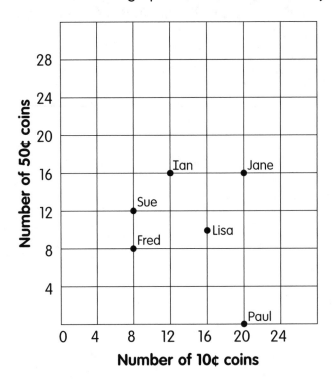

(a) Who has $5.60 in 10¢ and 20¢ coins?
(b) Who has $4.20 in 10¢ and 20¢ coins?
(c) Who has twice as much money in 20¢ as in 10¢ coins?
(d) Who has 20¢ more in 20¢ coins than in 10¢ coins?
(e) Which two people have the same amount of money?
(f) Which two people have a total amount of $7.20?

# Challenging Problems

## Worked Example 1

On a math test, a class of 21 students scored an average of 97 points. The maximum possible score of the test is 100 points. What is the least possible score that any of the 21 students could have obtained?

If all but one student had scored the maximum possible score, then the remaining student would have scored the least possible score.

Least possible points scored = 2,037 − (20 × 100)
= 37

The least possible score that any of the 21 students could have obtained is **37**.

# Worked Example 2

Find the average of the whole numbers from 1 to 100.

**Method 1**

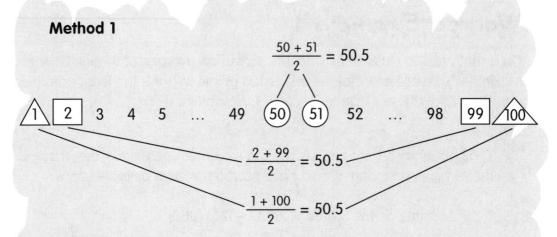

The average of each pair of numbers is 50.5.

Hence, the average of the whole numbers from 1 to 100 is **50.5**.

**Method 2**

Sum of the 100 whole numbers

$= 1 + 2 + 3 + \cdots + 98 + 99 + 100$

$= (1 + 100) + (2 + 99) + (3 + 98) + \cdots + (50 + 51)$

$=$ there are $\dfrac{100}{2}$ pairs, each with a sum of 101

$= 50 \times 101$

Average of the whole numbers from 1 to 100

$= \dfrac{50 \times 101}{100 \quad 2}$

$= \dfrac{101}{2}$

$= \mathbf{50.5}$

**Answer all questions. Show your work and write your statements clearly.**

1. Maria scored an average of 90 points on six tests. The total score of each test was 100 points. Find the lowest possible score she could have obtained.

   Hint: Refer to Worked Example 1.

2. Find the average of the whole numbers from 1 to 1,000.

   Hint: Refer to Worked Example 2.

3. Twelve cinemas have an average of 800 customers each day. Four of the cinemas close down but the total number of customers remains the same. What is the new average number of customers?

4. The average height of Esther, Felicia, and George is 151 cm. Esther is 8 cm shorter than Felicia, and George is 19 cm taller than Esther. Find the height of Esther, Felicia, and George.

Hint: Draw a model diagram.

5. There are 5 packages in a room. The masses of the packages are in whole numbers. If each package has a different mass, and the average mass of the packages is 16 kg, what is the heaviest that a package could be?

Hint: The lightest that a package could be is 1 kg.

6. The average mass of a group of adults is 72 kg. Four-ninths of the adults are men, and the rest are women. The average mass of the men is 82 kg. What is the average mass of the women?

   Hint: Let the number of adults be a multiple of 9.

7. The average of 16 consecutive odd numbers is 122. Find the smallest odd number.

   Hint: The average lies between the 8th and 9th terms.

8. The average of 10 consecutive odd numbers is 100. Find the sum of the smallest and greatest odd numbers.

   Hint: The average lies between the 5th and 6th terms.

9.  The average test score of Aaron and Bob is 16. The average test score of Bob and Chris is 18. The average test score of Chris and Dawn is 21. What is the average test score of Aaron and Dawn?

    Hint: What are the total scores of Aaron and Bob, Bob and Chris, and Chris and Dawn respectively?

10. Tyler needs to score 100 points on his final math test of the year to improve his average score from 76 to 79. How many math tests are there in the year?

11. Plot the points A(1,4), B(3,6) and D(3,2) in the space provided below. If these are the three corners of the square ABCD, mark the fourth corner, and write down its coordinates.

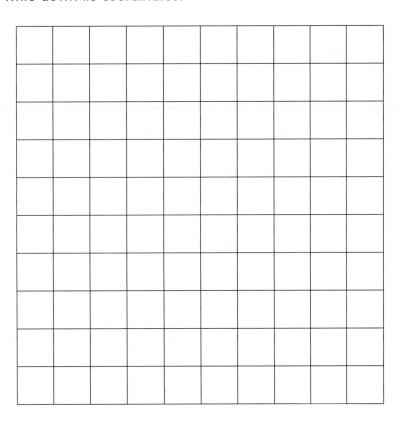

# 12 Rate

## Worked Example 1

The table below shows the rates of charges for a golf club membership. Roger wants to join the golf club for one and a half years. How much does he need to pay?

| One-time application fee | $1,450 |
|---|---|
| Monthly membership fee | $85 |

$1\frac{1}{2}$ years = 18 months

Membership fee for 18 months = 18 × $85
= $1,530

Total amount of money = $1,450 + $1,530
= $2,980

He needs to pay **$2,980**.

# Worked Example 2

Six men can pack 1,500 boxes in 4 days. At the same rate, how many boxes can eight men pack in 6 days?

### Method 1

Number of boxes 6 men can pack in 4 days ⟶ 1,500

Number of boxes 8 men can pack in 4 days ⟶ $\dfrac{1,500}{6} \times 8 = 2,000$

Number of boxes 8 men can pack in 6 days ⟶ $\dfrac{2,000}{4} \times 6 = 3,000$

Eight men can pack **3,000** boxes in 6 days.

### Method 2

Number of boxes 6 men can pack in 4 days ⟶ 1,500

Number of boxes 6 men can pack in 6 days ⟶ $\dfrac{1,500}{4} \times 6 = 2,250$

Number of boxes 8 men can pack in 6 days ⟶ $\dfrac{2,250}{6} \times 8 = 3,000$

Eight men can pack **3,000** boxes in 6 days.

Note: We may also use a table to present the information.

| Number of men | Number of days | Number of boxes |
|:---:|:---:|:---:|
| 6 | 4 | 1,500 |
| 6 | 6 | $\dfrac{1,500}{4} \times 6 = 2,250$ |
| 8 | 6 | $\dfrac{1,500}{4} \times 8 = 3,000$ |

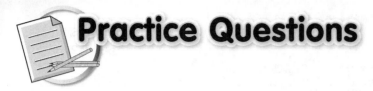

## Practice Questions

**Answer all questions. Show your work and write your statements clearly.**

1.  The table below shows the rates of charges at a parking lot.

    | For the first hour or part thereof | $2.80 |
    |---|---|
    | For every subsequent half an hour or part thereof | $2.20 |

    Glenn parked his car in the parking lot from 9:10 A.M. to 10:50 A.M. How much did he have to pay?

2.  Water flowing from a tap can fill a tub in 10 minutes. At this rate, how long does it take to fill the same tub from two similar taps?

3.  A photocopier can staple 360 booklets in 15 minutes.
    (a) How many booklets can the photocopier staple in 20 minutes?
    (b) How long would the photocopier take to staple 600 booklets?

4.  50 students have to pay $30 each to charter a bus. If there are
    only 40 students and the cost to charter a bus remains the same,
    how much will each student need to pay?

5.  Ann takes 8 minutes to run around the school track. Sophie can run
    around the school track eight times in 1 hour. Who is faster?

6. A machine produces 53 loaves of bread per hour. If the machine operates 24 hours a day, how many loaves of bread can the machine produce in 5 days?

7. The rent for 10 machines is $400 per month. The rent increases by a fixed amount for every additional 5 machines. The rent for 15 machines is $550 per month. At this rate, what is the rent for 25 machines?

8. A snail crawls along a ruler from the 16-cm mark to the 10-cm mark in 5 seconds. At this rate, how long will it take to reach the 1-cm mark from the 10-cm mark?

9. Ten workers can dig 20 holes in 40 days. At the same rate, how many days would twenty workers take to dig 10 holes?

Hint: Refer to Worked Example 2.

10. Three clerks can type six documents in 12 days. At this rate, how long will it take for two clerks to type three such documents?

# Challenging Problems

## Worked Example 1

Two pipes are used to fill a pool with water. Water flowing from the first pipe can fill the pool in 3 hours. Water flowing from the second pipe can fill the pool in 4 hours. If water is flowing out from both pipes, how long will it take to fill the pool?

**Method 1**

In 1 hour, water flowing from the first pipe can fill $\frac{1}{3}$ of the pool.

In 1 hour, water flowing from the second pipe can fill $\frac{1}{4}$ of the pool.

In 1 hour, water flowing from both pipes can fill $\frac{1}{3} + \frac{1}{4} = \frac{7}{12}$ of the pool.

$\frac{7}{12}$ of the pool can be filled by both pipes in 1 hour.

$\frac{12}{12}$ of the pool can be filled by both pipes in $\frac{12}{7} \times 1 = \frac{12}{7} = 1\frac{5}{7}$ hours.

It will take **$1\frac{5}{7}$ hours** to fill the pool with water.

**Method 2**

In 12 hours, the first pipe can fill $12 \div 3 = 4$ such pools.
In 12 hours, the second pipe can fill $12 \div 4 = 3$ such pools.
In 12 hours, the two pipes can fill $4 + 3 = 7$ such pools.

So, the two pipes can fill a pool in $\frac{12}{7} = 1\frac{5}{7}$ hours.

Hence, it will take both pipes **$1\frac{5}{7}$ hours** to fill up the pool.

**Answer all questions. Show your work and write your statements clearly.**

1. Clock A gains 5 minutes every hour and Clock B gains 8 minutes every hour. At noon, the minute hands of both clocks point at 12 at the same time. How many hours later will the minute hands of both clocks point at the same time again?

   Hint: How much faster is one clock over the other in one hour?

2. Tap A fills a tub with cold water in 6 minutes. Tap B fills the same tub with hot water in 8 minutes. If water is flowing out from taps A and B at the same time, how long does it take to fill the tub?

3. The cost for five guests to stay at a hotel for 7 days is $2,275. At this rate, how much will it cost three guests to stay at the same hotel for 4 days?

4. The table below shows the rates of charges for taxi fare in a city.

| For the first two km | $2.80 |
|---|---|
| For every subsequent 300 meters or part thereof | $0.30 |

If Clare had traveled a distance of 19.8 km, how much did she pay for the taxi fare?

5. In a hostel, there are 120 kg of rice for 80 travelers to consume for 12 days. Each traveler is given the same amount of rice every day.
   (a) If 16 new travelers join the hostel, how many days will the travelers take to consume 120 kg of rice?
   (b) If the hostel receives a donation of 40 kg of rice, how many days more will the 80 travelers take to consume them?

   Hint: (a) The amount of rice remains unchanged.
          (b) The number of travelers remains unchanged.

6. Three men take 2 days to paint 5 fences. At this rate, how many days will it take for two men to paint 1 fence?

   Challenge: Try different ways of solving this question.

7. Six men can pack 900 boxes in 4 days. At this rate, how many boxes can ten men pack in 6 days?

   Hint: Keep one variable constant, while working with the other two variables proportionately.

8. Aileen takes 2 days and Eve takes 3 days to sew 48 dresses altogether. If Aileen takes 4 days and Eve takes 2 days to sew 64 dresses altogether, how many days will each of them take to sew 48 dresses?

9. Simon takes 3 days and Lisa takes 1 day to paint $\frac{19}{20}$ of a house altogether. If Simon takes 4 days and Lisa takes 3 days to paint $1\frac{3}{5}$ houses altogether, how many days will each of them take to paint one house?

Hint: How many houses could be painted by Simon in 9 days and Lisa in 3 days, both working together?

10. Ben takes 6 days to renovate a room and James takes 15 days to renovate the same room. If James starts renovating the room first and leaves the rest of the renovation to be completed by Ben, they will take 9 days to complete renovating the room. At this rate, how many days will Ben take to complete the job?

## Worked Example 1

The line graph below shows the amount of rainfall in a town over a six-day period.

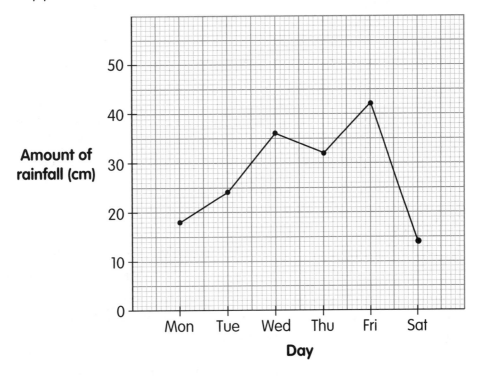

(a) What was the amount of rainfall on Wednesday?

(b) What was the greatest increase in the amount of rainfall between any two consecutive days?

(c) What was the greatest decrease in the amount of rainfall between any two consecutive days?

(a) The amount of rainfall on Wednesday was **36 cm**.

(b) To find the greatest increase in the amount of rainfall, locate the steepest upward slope.

The steepest upward slope occurred from Tuesday to Wednesday.

Greatest increase in the amount of rainfall = 36 cm – 24 cm
= 12 cm

The greatest increase in the amount of rainfall between any two consecutive days is **12 cm**.

Note: From Thursday to Friday, the increase was only 42 cm – 32cm = 10 cm.

(c) To find the greatest decrease in the amount of rainfall, locate the steepest downward slope.

The steepest downward slope occurred from Friday to Saturday.

Greatest decrease in the amount of rainfall = 42 cm – 14 cm
= 28 cm

The greatest decrease in the amount of rainfall between any two consecutive days is **28 cm**.

Note: For a line graph, only the value at each end-point is relevent, as the amount of rainfall does not fall proportionately during the course of a day.

# Worked Example 2

The line plot below shows the results of a survey on the number of children with a social media account in each household.

**Number of children in each household**

(a) How many households took part in the survey?
(b) What was the total number of children with a social media account in the households surveyed?
(c) What fraction of households has children without a social media account?

(a) From the line plot, there are a total of 16 dots.
So, **16** households took part in the survey.

(b) Total number of children involved in the survey
= (6 × 0) + (4 × 1) + (3 × 2) + (2 × 3) + (0 × 4) + (1 × 5)
= 0 + 4 + 6 + 6 + 0 + 5
= **21**

(c) Out of 16 households, 6 households have children without a social media account.

$$\frac{6}{16} = \frac{3}{8}$$

**Answer all questions. Show your work and write your statements clearly.**

1.  The bar graph below shows the number of fans of 5 football clubs.

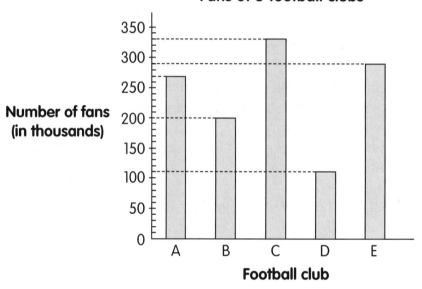

**Fans of 5 football clubs**

(a)  Express the number of fans from club D as a fraction of the total number of fans from clubs D and E.

(b)  If club C has 150,000 female fans, what is the ratio of the number of male fans to the number of female fans in club C?

(c)  What is the average number of fans?

2. The line graph below shows Jessie's earnings in the last 5 months.

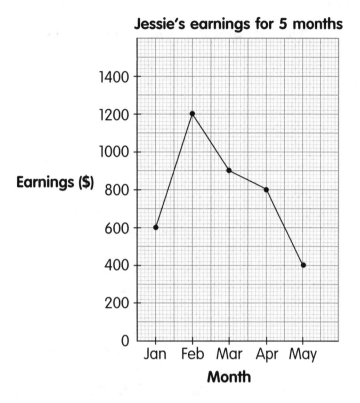

**Jessie's earnings for 5 months**

(a) How much more money did Jessie earn in February than in April?

(b) If Jessie saved $\frac{2}{5}$ of her January's earnings and $\frac{1}{3}$ of her February's earnings, how much money did she save?

(c) What was her average earnings from March to May?

3 . The histogram below shows the number of children each family has in a neighborhood.

**Number of children in a neighborhood**

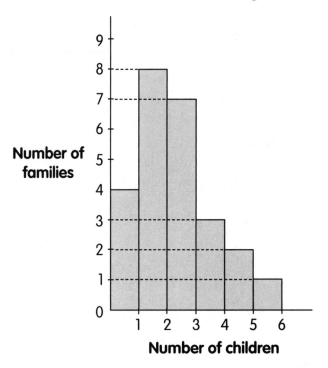

(a) What is the total number of families in the neighborhood?
(b) What fraction of the families have more than 3 children?
(c) Find the total number of children in the neighborhood.

4. The line graph below shows the number of stamps in 32 envelopes.

**Number of stamps in 32 envelopes**

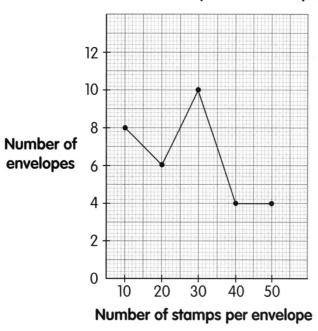

(a) How many envelopes contain less than 30 stamps?

(b) Pauline has some envelopes containing 40 stamps each. What would be the greatest possible number of stamps she could have?

(c) How many stamps are there altogether?

5.  The line plot below shows the number of smartphones per family in a given neighborhood.

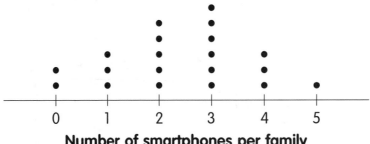

**Number of smartphones per family**

(a)  How many families live in this neighborhood?

(b)  How many smartphones are there altogether?

(c)  What fraction of families in the neighborhood has three or more smartphones in the family?

# Challenging Problems

## Worked Example 1

The distance between Town P and Town Q is 100 km. At 8:00 A.M., a car traveled from Town P to Town Q and a bus traveled from Town Q to Town P. The line graph below shows the journey of the car and the bus.

**Time taken for car and bus to travel between Town P and Town Q**

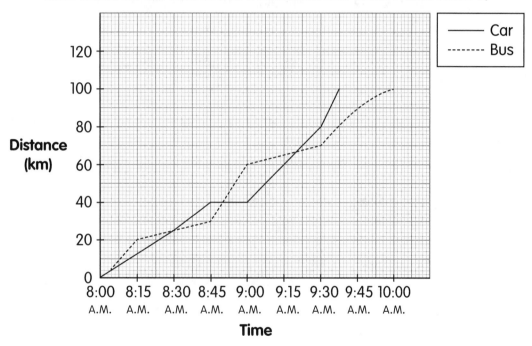

(a) How far away was the car from Town Q at 9:00 A.M.?

(b) How far apart were the car and the bus at 8:30 A.M.?

(c) At what time did the bus travel $\frac{1}{5}$ of the journey?

(a)  Distance that the car had traveled at 9:00 A.M. = 40 km

Distance away from Town Q = 100 km − 40 km
$$= 60 \text{ km}$$

The car was **60 km** away from Town Q at 9:00 A.M.

(b)  At 8:30 A.M., the car had traveled 25 km from Town P.

At 8:30 A.M., the bus had traveled 25 km from Town Q.

Distance apart
= 75 km − 25 km          or          100 km − (25 km + 25 km)
= 50 km                                        = 50 km

The bus and the car were **50 km** apart at 8:30 A.M.

(c)  $\frac{1}{5}$ of the journey represents a distance of $\frac{1}{5} \times 100 = 20$ km.

To know the time when the bus had traveled 20 km from Town Q, locate the time at the 20-km mark on the line graph.

The bus traveled $\frac{1}{5}$ of the journey at **8:15 A.M.**

**Answer all questions. Show your work and write your statements clearly.**

1. The distance between Town X and Town Y is 80 miles. At 7:00 A.M., a car traveled from Town X to Town Y and a truck traveled from Town Y to Town X. The line graph below shows the journey of the car and the truck.

**Time taken for car and truck to travel between Town X and Town Y**

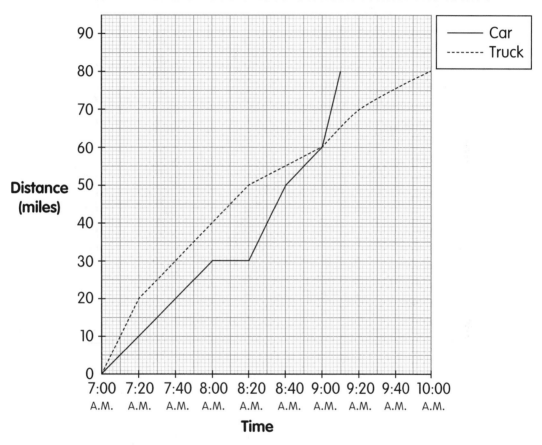

(a) How far away was the truck from Town X at 8:20 A.M.?
(b) At 8:40 A.M., how far were the car and the truck away from their destinations?
(c) At what time did the truck travel $\frac{3}{4}$ of the journey?

2 . The bar graph below shows the number of students who voted on their favorite and least favorite math topics.

**Students' favorite and least favorite math topics**

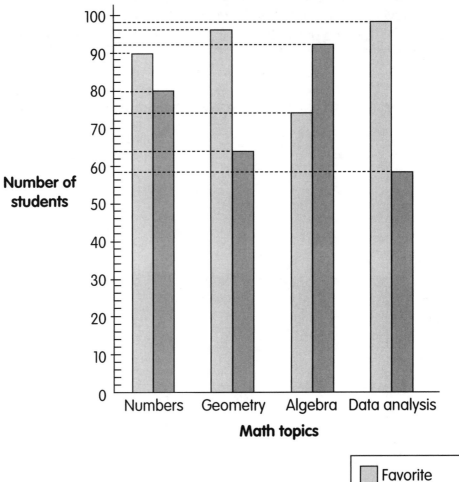

(a) Which topic was the most popular among the students?
(b) Which topic was the least popular among the students?
(c) Find the total number of students who chose algebra and geometry as their least favorite topics.
(d) Which topic had the second highest number of students who liked it?

# 14 Review Questions

## Worked Example 1

A tank was $\frac{3}{4}$-filled with fuel. When $\frac{1}{3}$ of the fuel was left, Scott poured in 450 gallons of fuel to fill up the tank. How many gallons of fuel can the tank contain?

**Method 1**

Amount of fuel at first

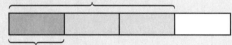

Amount of fuel left

To fill up the tank, Scott pours in 3 units of fuel.

3 units &longrightarrow; 450
1 unit &longrightarrow; 450 ÷ 3 = 150
4 units &longrightarrow; 4 × 150 = 600

The tank can contain **600** gallons of fuel.

**Method 2**

Fraction of fuel left in the tank = $\frac{1}{3} \times \frac{3}{4} = \frac{1}{4}$

Fraction of fuel representing 450 gallons = $1 - \frac{1}{4} = \frac{3}{4}$

$\frac{3}{4}$ of tank represents 450 gallons.

$\frac{4}{4}$ of tank represents $\frac{450}{3} \times 4 = 600$ gallons.

The tank can contain **600** gallons of fuel.

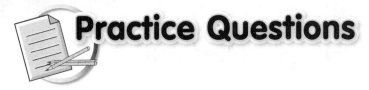

# Practice Questions

**Answer all questions. Show your work and write your statements clearly.**

1.  If Beth gave $1 to Ruth, Ruth would have twice as much as Beth.
    If Ruth gave $1 to Beth, they would have the same amount of money.
    How much did each of them have?

2.  Sally thinks of a number. When she multiplies the number by itself and then adds 10.01, she gets 91.01. What is Sally's number?

3. When a whole number is multiplied by another whole number, the product is 377. Both numbers are greater than 1. What are the two numbers?

4. Betty and Joshua had $200 in all. After Betty spent $50 and Joshua lost $80, they each had the same amount of money. How much did Joshua have at first?

5.  The table below shows the number of short-sighted and long-sighted boys and girls. Complete the table.

| | Short-sighted | Long-sighted | Total |
|---|---|---|---|
| **Number of boys** | 32 | | |
| **Number of girls** | | | 53 |
| **Total** | | 44 | 104 |

6.  A piece of paper, measuring 32 cm by 16 cm, is cut into half. Each of the pieces is cut into half again. The process is repeated until a piece measuring 2 cm by 1 cm is obtained. How many cuts are needed in all?

7. The solid below is made up of 6 identical cubes. Each cube has a side of 5 cm. What is the total surface area of the solid?

   Hint: Find the number of squares that make up the surface area of the solid.

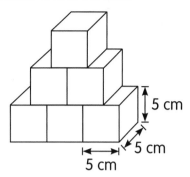

5 cm

5 cm

5 cm

8. Sam arranges 14 coins into 4 different rows. The first row has 3 more coins than the second row. The second row has 1 coin less than the third row. The fourth row has twice as many coins as the second row. Find the number of coins in each row.

   Hint: Assign the row with the fewest number of coins to one unit. Or use guess and check.

9.  The ratio of the number of Henry's pens to the number of Donald's pens was 3 : 5. After Donald gave away 35 pens to a charity, he had half as many pens as Henry. How many pens did Donald have at first?

10. The ratio of the area of Triangle P to the area of Triangle Q is 2 : 1. The ratio of the area of the shaded region to the area of the unshaded region is 1 : 1. Find the ratio of the area of Triangle Q to area of the unshaded region.

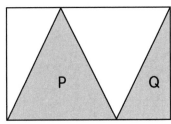

## Worked Example 1

In the figure below, PQRS is a rectangle and TPR is a triangle. If the ratio of the length of ST to the length of TR is 1 : 2, what is the ratio of the area of triangle TPR to the area of rectangle PQRS?

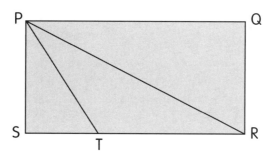

Since the ratio of the length of ST to the length of TR is 1 : 2, the length of SR is 3 units. Let the length of the rectangle be 3 units and the width of the rectangle be QR.

Area of rectangle PQRS = 3 × QR

Since the ratio of the length of ST to the length of TR is 1 : 2, the length of TR is 2 units. Let the base of the triangle be 2 units and the height of the triangle be QR.

Area of triangle TPR = $\frac{1}{2}$ × 2 × QR

= QR

The ratio of the area of triangle TPR to the area of rectangle PQRS is **1 : 3**.

**Answer all questions. Show your work and write your statements clearly.**

1. There are thirteen cards numbered 1 to 13. Tracy picks up three cards and finds that when the numbers on the cards are multiplied together, the product is 252. Which are the three cards?

   Hint: Express 252 as a product of prime factors.

2. Brian is given a list of clues to solve a 5-digit number puzzle.

   The clues are:
   (i)   All the digits are different.
   (ii)  The first digit is an odd number and it is greater than the third digit.
   (iii) The fourth digit is three times the value of the first digit.
   (iv)  The last digit is the product of the second and third digits.

   What is the number?

3.  In a family, the girls have twice as many sisters as brothers. The boys have five times as many sisters as brothers. How many boys and girls are there?

    Hint: Use guess and check.

4.  Alan and Amy are students in Singapore. They want to buy a pen. Alan needs 50¢ more and Amy needs 10¢ more. When they put their money together, they still do not have enough money to buy the pen. Assume that there are only 5¢, 10¢, 20¢, and 50¢ coins, how much does the pen cost?

5. Karen has a rectangular cardboard measuring 38 cm long and 27 cm wide. If she needs to cut some small rectangles, each 5 cm long and 3 cm wide, from the cardboard, how many small rectangles can she get?

6. The figure below shows a rectangular garden measuring 21 m by 15 m. Robert plans to lay square tiles measuring 1.5 m by 1.5 m on the shaded path. How many such tiles will he need?

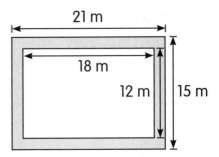

7. Paul is twice as old as Timothy this year. If their combined age is 54 years, what will be their combined age when Timothy is as old as Paul is this year?

8. Smith packed 8 apples into each basket and 20 apples into each box. If 560 apples were packed into 46 baskets and boxes altogether, find the number of boxes that he had.

   Hint: Use guess and check, or make a supposition.

9. Sandy divided a 2-digit number by another 2-digit number and obtained 0.78125 as the answer. Find the two numbers.

Hint: Express 0.78125 as a fraction in the simplest form.

10. There are 32 tennis players in a tennis tournament. If a player loses, he will be out of the tournament. If a player wins, he will proceed to the next round. How many matches are played before a winner emerges?

# Answers

## 1 Whole Numbers

### Practice Questions (pp. 3–5)

1. *Method 1*

| Aaron | Cathy | Esther | Ginny | Ian | Karen |
|-------|-------|--------|-------|-----|-------|
| 1 | 2 | 3 | 4 | 5 | 6 |
| 7 | 8 | 9 | 10 | 11 | 12 |
| ⋮ | ⋮ | ⋮ | ⋮ | ⋮ | ⋮ |
| 97 | 98 | 99 | 100 | | |

**Ginny** gets the last sticker from Mr. Lee.

*Method 2*
To determine who gets the last sticker, look at the remainder (R) obtained when the number of stickers is divided by 6 people.
$100 = 6 \times 16 + 4$
The last sticker will go to the 4th person in the circle, who is **Ginny**.

2.

| 2-digit number | Sum of digits |
|----------------|---------------|
| 15 | $1 + 5 = 6$ but $3 \times 6 \neq 15$ ✗ |
| 24 | $2 + 4 = 6$ but $3 \times 6 \neq 24$ ✗ |
| 27 | $2 + 7 = 9$ and $3 \times 9 = 27$ ✔ |

**27** is the number.

3. If there is no CD left over, the least possible number of CDs = $2 \times 3 \times 5 = 30$
Since there is always 1 CD left over, the least possible number of CDs Louis could have is $(30 + 1) = $ **31**

4. Page numbers that contain the digit 2: 2, 12, 20, 21, 22, 23, 24, 25, 26, 27, 28, 29, 32, 42, 52, 62, 72, 82, 92
Page numbers that contain the digit 2 but not divisible by 2: 21, 23, 25, 27, and 29.
**5** page numbers contain the digit 2 but are not divisible by 2.

5. Consider a puzzle with fewer pieces, e.g. 5 pieces. Joining all five pieces together could happen as follows:

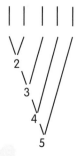

It will always take 4 moves to join a jigsaw puzzle with 5 pieces. Try with a few more cases, the number of moves will always be one less than the number of pieces. Hence, it will take **49** moves to join all 50 pieces.

6. Accept all correct answers.
(a) She threw **6** darts.
(b) All 6 darts landed on **19**, **19**, **19**, **19**, **12**, and **12**.

7. Number of games played in all
$= 5 + 4 + 3 + 2 + 1 = $ **15**

8. Difference = $502 - 397 = 105$
New sum = $2,783 + 105 = $ **2,888**

9.
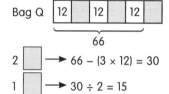

$2\ \square \longrightarrow 66 - (3 \times 12) = 30$

$1\ \square \longrightarrow 30 \div 2 = 15$

Number of toys she added to each bag
= **15**

### Challenging Problems (pp. 7–10)

1. Number $X = (16 \times$ Number $Y) + 3$

| X |
|---|

| Y | ... | Y | 3 |

16 units

Let $\boxed{Y}$ be 1 unit.
Number $Y = 1$ unit
Number $X = 16$ units $+ 3$
$16$ units $+ 3 + 1$ unit $+ 16 + 3 \longrightarrow 345$
$17$ units $\longrightarrow 323$
$1$ unit $\longrightarrow 323 \div 17 = 19$
Number $X = (16 \times 19) + 3 = $ **307**

2. The next palindromic number after $12,321$
$= 12,421$
$12,421 - 12,321 = 100$
His speed = $100 \div 2 = $ **50 km/h**

3. $770 = 2 \times 5 \times 7 \times 11$
Since the ages are those of two adults, their possible ages are $2 \times 11 = 22$ and $5 \times 7 = 35$.
Sum of their ages = $22 + 35$
$= $ **57 years**

**4.**

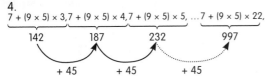

$7 + (9 \times 5) \times 3, 7 + (9 \times 5) \times 4, 7 + (9 \times 5) \times 5, \ldots 7 + (9 \times 5) \times 22,$

142  187  232  997

+ 45  + 45  + 45

The numbers are 142, 187, …, 952 and 997.
Numbers of such 3-digit numbers = 22 – 3 + 1
= **20**

**5.**

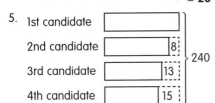

1st candidate

2nd candidate  8

3rd candidate  13    240

4th candidate  15

8 + 13 + 15 = 36
4 units ⟶ 240 + 36 = 276
1 unit ⟶ 276 ÷ 4 = 69
Lowest number of votes received by a candidate = 69 – 15 = **54**

**6.**

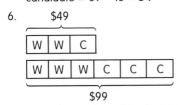

$49

| W | W | C |

| W | W | W | C | C | C |

$99

Cost of 1 watch and 1 calculator
= $99 ÷ 3 = $33
Cost of 1 watch = $49 – $33 = **$16**

**7.**

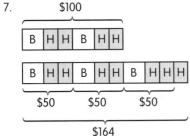

$100

| B | H | H | B | H | H |

| B | H | H | B | H | H | B | H | H | H |

$50   $50   $50

$164

Cost of 1 bag and 2 hats   = $100 ÷ 2
= $50
Cost of 3 bags and 6 hats  = 3 × $50
= $150
Cost of 1 hat = $164 – $150 = **$14**

**8.** 8 watches and 8 lamps
= $176 + $208 = $384

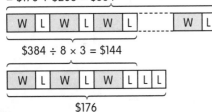

| W | L | W | L | W | L |   | W | L |

$384 ÷ 8 × 3 = $144

| W | L | W | L | W | L | L | L |

$176

Cost of 8 watches and 8 lamps
= $176 + $208 = $384

Cost of 1 watch and 1 lamp
= $384 ÷ 8 = $48
Cost of 3 watches and 3 lamps
= 3 × $48 = $144
Cost of 2 lamps = $176 – $144 = $32
Cost of 1 lamp = $32 ÷ 2 = **$16**

**9.** 1 mug

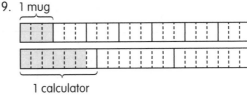

1 calculator

4 ☐ ⟶ $12
1 ☐ ⟶ $12 ÷ 4 = $3
3 ☐ ⟶ 3 × $3 = $9
Cost of 1 mug = **$9**

**10.** 1 jacket                    1 unit

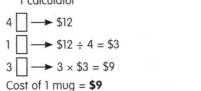

1 shirt
2 units ⟶ $16
1 unit ⟶ $16 ÷ 2 = $8
3 units ⟶ 3 × $8 = $24
Cost of 1 shirt = **$24**

# 2  Fractions

**Practice Questions** (pp. 13–15)

1. $\frac{1}{2} + \frac{1}{3} + \frac{1}{4} = \frac{6}{12} + \frac{4}{12} + \frac{3}{12}$

$= \frac{13}{12}$ or $1\frac{1}{12}$

The total mass is $1\frac{1}{12}$ **kg.**

2. $23\frac{1}{4} - 9\frac{2}{5} = 14\frac{1}{4} - \frac{2}{5}$

$= 14\frac{5}{20} - \frac{8}{20}$

$= 13\frac{25}{20} - \frac{8}{20}$

$= 13\frac{17}{20}$

The blue string is $13\frac{17}{20}$ **cm** longer.

3. $\frac{2}{5} \times 3$ km $= \frac{6}{5}$ km

$= \frac{6}{5} \times 1000$ m

$= 1200$ m

She ran **1200 m.**

4. *Method 1*

$2\frac{1}{3}$ cm $+ 2\frac{1}{3}$ cm $+ 2\frac{1}{3}$ cm $= 7$ cm

A 7-cm strip of paper yields 3 smaller pieces.

7 cm $\longrightarrow$ 3 pieces

21 cm $\longrightarrow$ 3 × 3 = 9 pieces

Number of pieces Tommy will have = **9**

*Method 2*

$2\frac{1}{3} = \frac{7}{3}$

Number of pieces Tommy will have $= 21 \div \frac{7}{3}$

$$= 21 \times \frac{3}{7}$$
$$= \mathbf{9}$$

5.

bag of flour

1 unit $\longrightarrow$ 1 kg

2 units $\longrightarrow$ 2 × 1 kg = 2 kg

Mass of 2 similar bags of flour = 2 × 2 kg

$\qquad\qquad\qquad\qquad\qquad\qquad = \mathbf{4\ kg}$

6.

| book | candy | $2 |

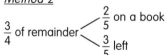

1 unit $\longrightarrow$ $2

2 units $\longrightarrow$ 2 × $2 = $4

He paid **$4** for the book.

7. *Method 1*

shirt    book    ?

(a) Fraction of his allowance left $= \dfrac{9}{20}$

(b) 6 units $\longrightarrow$ $18

1 unit $\longrightarrow$ $18 ÷ 6 = $3

20 units $\longrightarrow$ 20 × $3 = $60

Amount of allowance he had at first

$= \mathbf{\$60}$

*Method 2*

$\frac{3}{4}$ of remainder $\begin{cases} \frac{2}{5} \text{ on a book} \\ \frac{3}{5} \text{ left} \end{cases}$

(a) Fraction of his allowance left after buying

a shirt $= 1 - \dfrac{1}{4} = \dfrac{3}{4}$

Fraction of his allowance left after buying

a shirt and a book $= \dfrac{3}{5} \times \dfrac{3}{4} = \dfrac{\mathbf{9}}{\mathbf{20}}$

(b) Fraction of his allowance spent on

a book $= \dfrac{2}{5} \times \dfrac{3}{4} = \dfrac{6}{20}$

$\dfrac{6}{20}$ of his allowance $\longrightarrow$ $18

$\dfrac{1}{20}$ of his allowance $\longrightarrow$ $18 ÷ 6 = $3

$\dfrac{20}{20}$ of his allowance $\longrightarrow$ 20 × $3 = $60

Amount of allowance he had at first = **$60**

8. $\dfrac{2}{5} = \dfrac{4}{10}$

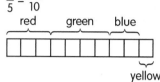

Difference between the number of red marbles and the number of blue marbles = 1 unit

1 unit $\longrightarrow$ 17

10 units $\longrightarrow$ 10 × 17 = 170

Total number of marbles = **170**

## Challenging Problems (pp. 18–22)

1. Other than comparing each fraction with $\frac{1}{5}$, we can also multiply each fraction by 5 and compare with 1.

$\dfrac{5}{21} \times 5 = \dfrac{25}{21}$, which is greater than 1.

$\dfrac{7}{36} \times 5 = \dfrac{35}{36}$, which is less than 1.

$\dfrac{15}{72} \times 5 = \dfrac{75}{72}$, which is greater than 1.

$\dfrac{26}{101} \times 5 = \dfrac{130}{101}$, which is greater than 1.

Since $\dfrac{35}{36}$ is less than 1, $\dfrac{\mathbf{7}}{\mathbf{36}}$ is less than $\dfrac{1}{5}$.

2. From observing the pattern, we know that

$$\frac{x-2}{x-1} = \frac{2,013}{2,014} = \frac{2,015-2}{2,015-1}$$

Hence, the value of $x$ is **2,015**.

3. $\dfrac{N}{D} = \dfrac{2}{3}$; N × D = 216

216 = 2 × 2 × 2 × 3 × 3 × 3

$\dfrac{N}{D} = \dfrac{2}{3} \times \left(\dfrac{2}{3} \times \dfrac{3}{2}\right) = \dfrac{\mathbf{12}}{\mathbf{18}}$

4.

Jim

Shirley

52

8 units $\longrightarrow$ 260 − 52 = 208

1 unit $\longrightarrow$ 208 ÷ 8 = 26

Jim gave 26 coins to Shirley.
4 units → 4 × 26 = 104
Number of coins Shirley had at first
= 104 + (52 − 26) = **130**

5.

Ryan

Marie

75

15

5 units → 75 − 15 = 60
1 unit → 60 ÷ 5 = 12
8 units → 8 × 12 = 96
Number of marbles Ryan had at first
= 96 + 15 = **111**

6.
Kevin
Ruth
} $115

Bob
Ruth
} $130

1 unit → $130 − $115 = $15
2 units → 2 × $15 = $30
Amount of money Ruth has
= $115 − $30 = **$85**

7.
Steve
Larry
} 171
39

10 units → 171 + 39 = 210
1 unit → 210 ÷ 10 = 21
7 units → 7 × 21 = 147
Number of marbles Steve has = **147**

8.
Farm A
Farm B
} 845

13 units → 845
1 unit → 845 ÷ 13 = 65
8 units → 8 × 65 = 520
Number of sheep on Farm B = **520**

9.
Martha
Mary
24
} 375

13 units → 375 − 24 = 351
1 unit → 351 ÷ 13 = 27
7 units → 7 × 27 = 189
6 units → 6 × 27 = 162
Number of jelly beans Martha had = **189**
Number of jelly beans Mary had = 162 + 24
= **186**

10. In 1 h, the first man can complete $\frac{1}{6}$ of the task, the second man can complete $\frac{1}{4}$ of the task, and the third man can complete $\frac{1}{3}$ of the task.
In 1 h, all three men can complete
$$= \frac{1}{6} + \frac{1}{4} + \frac{1}{3} = \frac{9}{12}$$
$$= \frac{3}{4} \text{ of the task}$$

$\frac{3}{4}$ of the task → 1 h

$\frac{1}{4}$ of the task → $1 \div 3 = \frac{1}{3}$ h

$\frac{4}{4}$ of the task → $4 \times \frac{1}{3} = \frac{4}{3} = 1\frac{1}{3}$ h

The 3 men will take **$1\frac{1}{3}$ h** to complete the task.

# 3 Area and Perimeter

**Practice Questions** (pp. 26–28)

1. Perimeter of rectangle = 78 cm
Length + width = 78 cm ÷ 2 = 39 cm
Length = 39 cm − 17 cm = 22 cm
Area of rectangle = Length × width
= 22 cm × 17 cm
**= 374 cm²**

2.

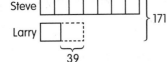

3          3

5

5

From the diagram, **4** smaller rectangles can be cut from the larger rectangle.

3.

600 cm

800 cm

Length → $\frac{600}{10}$ = 60 squares

Width → $\frac{800}{10}$ = 80 squares

Hence, 60 × 80 = **4,800** square tiles are needed to cover the floor.

4. Length of one side of the square floor
= 32 m ÷ 4 = 8 m
Area of square floor = 8 m × 8 m
= 64 m²
Cost of carpeting the floor = 64 × $8
= **$512**

5. Width + length of rectangle = 50 cm ÷ 2
= 25 cm
Width of rectangle = 25 cm – 16 cm
= 9 cm
Area of rectangle = 16 cm × 9 cm
= 144 cm²
Area of square = 144 cm²
= 12 cm × 12 cm
Length of the square = **12 cm**

6.
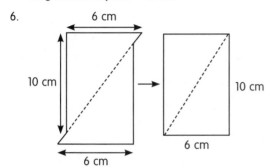
Area = 10 cm × 6 cm = **60 cm²**

7. Area of one rectangle = 25 cm × 8 cm
= 200 cm²
Area of figure = Area of two rectangles
– Area of middle square
= (2 × 200 cm²)
– (8 cm × 8 cm)
= 400 cm² – 64 cm²
= **336 cm²**

8. *Method 1*
Along the length of the land, there are
55 ÷ 5 = 11 intervals of 5 m each. Therefore,
he can plant 11 + 1 = 12 trees.
Along the width of the land, there are
30 ÷ 5 = 6 intervals of 5 m each. Therefore,
he can plant 6 + 1 = 7 trees.
At each corner, the same tree lies along
each length and width; so, there are a
total of 4 trees shared by both lengths
and widths.
Number of trees he can plant
= 2 × (12 + 7) – 4 = **34**

*Method 2*
(55 ÷ 5) + 1 = 12 trees
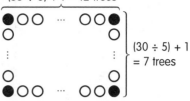
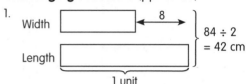
(30 ÷ 5) + 1
= 7 trees
Number of trees he can plant
= 2 × 12 + 2 × (7 – 2) = **34**

## Challenging Problems (pp. 31–35)

1.
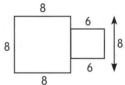
Width
Length
1 unit
84 ÷ 2
= 42 cm

2 units → 42 + 8 = 50
1 unit → 50 ÷ 2 = 25
Length of rectangle = 25 cm
Width of rectangle = 25 – 8 = 17 cm
Area of rectangle = Length × width
= 25 cm × 17 cm
= **425 cm²**

2. 64 = 8 × 8
Length of larger square = 8 cm
36 = 6 × 6
Length of smaller square = 6 cm
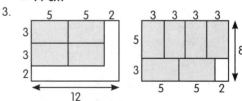
Perimeter of the figure
= 8 cm × 4 + 6 cm × 2
= 32 cm + 12 cm
= **44 cm**

3.
From the two diagrams, the maximum
number of rectangles = **6**.

4.

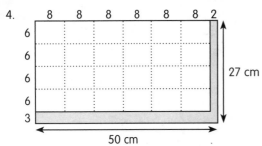

8 8 8 8 8 8 2

27 cm

50 cm

4 × 6 = 24 rectangles

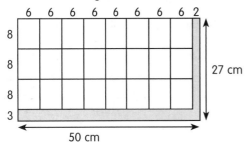

6 6 6 6 6 6 6 2

27 cm

50 cm

3 × 8 = 24 rectangles

Both diagrams show that a maximum
of **24** rectangles can be cut from it.

5. Divide one side of the square into 5 cm and
7 cm and the other side of the square into
4 cm and 8 cm.

6. There are 2 possible answers.
Two square numbers, which have
a difference of 80, are 64 and 144.
$64 \text{ cm}^2 = 8 \text{ cm} \times 8 \text{ cm}$
$144 \text{ cm}^2 = 12 \text{ cm} \times 12 \text{ cm}$
Perimeter of figure
= 12 cm + 12 cm + 12 cm + 8 cm + 8 cm
+ 8 cm + 4 cm
= **64 cm**

The other two square numbers, which have
a difference of 80, are 1 and 81.
$1 \text{ cm}^2 = 1 \text{ cm} \times 1 \text{ cm}$
$81 \text{ cm}^2 = 9 \text{ cm} \times 9 \text{ cm}$
Perimeter of figure
= 9 cm × 4 + 1 cm × 2 = **38 cm**

7. There are 2 possible answers.
$376 \text{ cm}^2 = (13 \text{ cm} \times 7 \text{ cm}) + (19 \text{ cm} \times 15 \text{ cm})$
$= 91 \text{ cm}^2 + 285 \text{ cm}^2$
Difference in areas = 285 cm² – 91 cm²
= **194 cm²**

$376 \text{ cm}^2 = (13 \text{ cm} \times 26 \text{ cm}) +$
$(19 \text{ cm} \times 2 \text{ cm})$
$= 338 \text{ cm}^2 + 38 \text{ cm}^2$
Difference in areas = 338 cm² – 38 cm²
= **300 cm²**

8. Area of each rectangle = 200 cm² ÷ 4
= 50 cm²
Length = 2 × width
Using the guess and check method,

| Width (cm) | Length (cm) | Area (cm²) | Is the area of each rectangle 50 cm²? |
|---|---|---|---|
| 3 | 6 | 18 | No |
| 4 | 8 | 32 | No |
| **5** | **10** | **50** | **Yes** |

*Method 1*
Perimeter = 4 × (10 cm + 5 cm + 5 cm)
= **80 cm**

*Method 2*
Perimeter = 5 cm + 5 cm + 10 cm + 5 cm +
5 cm + 10 cm + 5 cm + 5 cm +
10 cm + 5 cm + 5 cm + 10 cm
= **80 cm**

9. Area of larger square = 8 cm × 8 cm
= 64 cm²
Area of smaller square = 6 cm × 6 cm
= 36 cm²
Area of shaded region = 5 cm × 4 cm
= 20 cm²
Area of unshaded region
= 64 cm² + 36 cm² – 2 × 20 cm²
= 100 cm² – 40 cm²
= **60 cm²**

10. Length of figure = 8 widths of a rectangle
= 5 lengths of a rectangle
Width of figure = 1 length + 1 width
$= 1 \text{ length} + \frac{5}{8} \text{ length}$
$= \frac{13}{8} \text{ lengths}$
Area of figure $= 5 \text{ lengths} \times \frac{13}{8} \text{ lengths}$
$= 5 \times \frac{13}{8} \text{ length} \times \text{length}$
$= \frac{65}{8} \times \text{length} \times \text{length}$
$= 520 \text{ cm}^2$

Length × length $= \frac{520 \times 8}{65}$
$= 64 \text{ cm}^2$
$= 8 \text{ cm} \times 8 \text{ cm}$
Length of rectangle = 8 cm
Perimeter of figure
$= (5 \text{ lengths} + \frac{13}{8} \text{ lengths}) \times 2$
$= [(5 \times 8 \text{ cm}) + (\frac{13}{8} \times 8 \text{ cm})] \times 2$
= **106 cm**

## 4 Area of Triangles

### Practice Questions (pp. 41–44)

1. Length of third side = 30 – 13 – 12
   $$= 5 \text{ cm}$$
   Area of triangle $= \frac{1}{2} \times 12 \text{ cm} \times 5 \text{ cm}$
   $$= \textbf{30 cm}^2$$

2.

   From the diagram, the maximum number of triangles = **8**.

3. AE is the base of triangles ABE, ACE, and ADE. Since BD is parallel to AE, triangles ABE, ACE, and ADE have the same height. Since triangles ABE, ACE, and ADE have the same base and height, they have the same area.

4. Area of figure
   = 2 × Area of triangle XYZ
   $$= 2 \times \left[ \frac{1}{2} \times 18 \text{ cm} \times (10 \text{ cm} \div 2) \right]$$
   $$= \textbf{90 cm}^2$$

5. *Method 1*
   Area of unshaded region
   $$= \left( \frac{1}{2} \times 17 \text{ cm} \times 17 \text{ cm} \right) + \left( \frac{1}{2} \times 9 \text{ cm} \times 17 \text{ cm} \right)$$
   $$= 144\frac{1}{2} \text{ cm}^2 + 76\frac{1}{2} \text{ cm}^2$$
   $$= \textbf{221 cm}^2$$

   *Method 2*
   Area of unshaded region
   $$= (17 \text{ cm} \times 17 \text{ cm}) - \left( \frac{1}{2} \times (17 \text{ cm} - 9 \text{ cm}) \times 17 \text{ cm} \right)$$
   $$= 289 \text{ cm}^2 - 68 \text{ cm}^2$$
   $$= \textbf{221 cm}^2$$

6. Area of triangle AEF
   = area of square ABCD – area of triangle ABE – area of triangle ADF – area of triangle ECF
   $$= (12 \text{ cm} \times 12 \text{ cm}) - \left( \frac{1}{2} \times 12 \text{ cm} \times 6 \text{ cm} \right) - \left( \frac{1}{2} \times 12 \text{ cm} \times 6 \text{ cm} \right) - \left( \frac{1}{2} \times 6 \text{ cm} \times 6 \text{ cm} \right)$$
   $$= 144 \text{ cm}^2 - 36 \text{ cm}^2 - 36 \text{ cm}^2 - 18 \text{ cm}^2$$
   $$= \textbf{54 cm}^2$$

7. Area of square = 7 cm × 7 cm = 49 cm²
   Area of two small unshaded triangles
   $$= 2 \times \left( \frac{1}{2} \times 2 \text{ cm} \times 2 \text{ cm} \right)$$
   $$= 4 \text{ cm}^2$$
   Area of two large unshaded triangles
   $$= 2 \times \left( \frac{1}{2} \times 5 \text{ cm} \times 5 \text{ cm} \right)$$
   $$= 25 \text{ cm}^2$$
   Area of shaded region
   = 49 cm² – 4 cm² – 25 cm² = **20 cm²**

8. Perimeter of figure
   = 30 cm + 12 cm + 25 cm + 13 cm
   = 80 cm
   *Method 1*
   Area of figure
   = (25 cm × 12 cm) +
   $$\left( \frac{1}{2} \times (30 \text{ cm} - 25 \text{ cm}) \times 12 \text{ cm} \right)$$
   = 300 cm² + 30 cm²
   = **330 cm²**

   *Method 2*
   Form a new rectangle by creating another identical figure.

   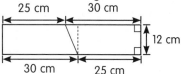

   Area of figure $= \frac{1}{2} \times$ area of new rectangle
   $$= \frac{1}{2} \times (30 \text{ cm} + 25 \text{ cm}) \times 12 \text{ cm}$$
   $$= \textbf{330 cm}^2$$

### Challenging Problems (pp. 47–52)

1. Area of triangle ABC $= \frac{1}{2} \times 8 \text{ cm} \times 8 \text{ cm}$
   $$= 32 \text{ cm}^2$$
   Area of triangle AEF
   $$= \frac{1}{2} \times (8 \text{ cm} + 6 \text{ cm}) \times 6 \text{ cm}$$
   $$= 42 \text{ cm}^2$$
   Area of shaded region
   = (8 cm × 8 cm) + (6 cm × 6 cm) – 32 cm² – 42 cm²
   = 64 cm² + 36 cm² – 32 cm² – 42 cm²
   = **26 cm²**

2.

   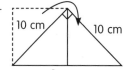

   Area $= \frac{1}{2} \times 10 \text{ cm} \times 10 \text{ cm} = \textbf{50 cm}^2$

3. Step 1: Divide each square into quarters.

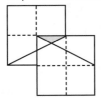

Step 2: Divide each quarter into four rectangles.

The figure is made up of 28 rectangles. Since the area of the shaded region is half that of a rectangle, the fraction of the figure that is shaded is $\frac{1}{2} \times \frac{1}{28} = \frac{1}{56}$.

4. Area of A = Area of B = $\frac{1}{4}$ **m²**

Area of C = Area of E = $\frac{1}{16}$ **m²**

Area of D = Area of F = Area of G = $\frac{1}{8}$ **m²**

5.

Divide the figure into triangles that are identical to triangle CDE.
Fraction of triangle ABD that is shaded = $\frac{1}{16}$

6. Divide the figure into triangles as shown below.

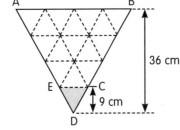

Fraction of figure that is shaded = $\frac{8}{32} = \frac{1}{4}$

7. Area of triangle PTV
$= \frac{1}{2} \times (10 \text{ cm} + 6 \text{ cm}) \times 10 \text{ cm} = 80 \text{ cm}^2$
Area of triangle PQR
$= \frac{1}{2} \times 10 \text{ cm} \times (10 \text{ cm} - 6 \text{ cm}) = 20 \text{ cm}^2$

Area of triangle RST $= \frac{1}{2} \times 6 \text{ cm} \times 6 \text{ cm}$
$= 18 \text{ cm}^2$
Area of shaded region
$= (10 \text{ cm} \times 10 \text{ cm}) + (6 \text{ cm} \times 6 \text{ cm})$
$\quad - 80 \text{ cm}^2 - 20 \text{ cm}^2 - 18 \text{ cm}^2$
$= \textbf{18 cm}^2$

8.

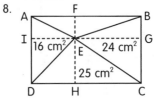

Since AD = BC and IE = DH,
Area of triangle AED $= \frac{1}{2} \times AD \times IE$
$= \frac{1}{2} \times AD \times DH$
$= 16 \text{ cm}^2$
Area of rectangle AFHD = AD × DH
$= 2 \times 16 \text{ cm}^2$
$= 32 \text{ cm}^2$

Since EG = HC,
Area of triangle EBC $= \frac{1}{2} \times BC \times EG$
$= \frac{1}{2} \times BC \times HC$
$= 24 \text{ cm}^2$
Area of rectangle FBCH = BC × HC
$= 2 \times 24 \text{ cm}^2$
$= 48 \text{ cm}^2$
Area of rectangle ABCD = 32 cm² + 48 cm²
$= 80 \text{ cm}^2$

Area of triangle ABE
$= 80 \text{ cm}^2 - 16 \text{ cm}^2 - 25 \text{ cm}^2 - 24 \text{ cm}^2$
$= \textbf{15 cm}^2$

9.

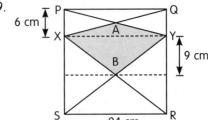

$PX = \frac{1}{4} PS = \frac{1}{4} \times 24 = 6 \text{ cm}$
XS = 18 cm
Height of triangle B = 18 cm ÷ 2 = 9 cm

Area of triangle A $= \frac{1}{2} \times XY \times \frac{1}{2} PX$

$\quad\quad = \frac{1}{2} \times 24 \text{ cm} \times 3 \text{ cm}$

$\quad\quad = 36 \text{ cm}^2$

Area of triangle B $= \frac{1}{2} \times XY \times 9 \text{ cm}$

$\quad\quad = \frac{1}{2} \times 24 \text{ cm} \times 9 \text{ cm}$

$\quad\quad = 108 \text{ cm}^2$

Area of shaded region $= 36 \text{ cm}^2 + 108 \text{ cm}^2$

$\quad\quad\quad\quad\quad\quad = \textbf{144 cm}^2$

10.

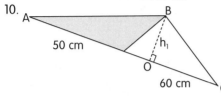

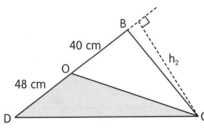

$\dfrac{\text{Area of } \triangle OAB}{\text{Area of } \triangle OCB} = \dfrac{\frac{1}{2} \times 50 \times h_1}{\frac{1}{2} \times 60 \times h_1} = \dfrac{5}{6}$

$\dfrac{\text{Area of } \triangle OCD}{\text{Area of } \triangle OCB} = \dfrac{\frac{1}{2} \times 48 \times h_2}{\frac{1}{2} \times 40 \times h_2} = \dfrac{6}{5}$

$\dfrac{\text{Area of } \triangle OAB}{\text{Area of } \triangle OCD}$

$= \dfrac{\text{Area of } \triangle OAB}{\text{Area of } \triangle OCB} \times \dfrac{\text{Area of } \triangle OCB}{\text{Area of } \triangle OCD}$

$= \dfrac{5}{6} \times \dfrac{5}{6}$

$= \dfrac{\textbf{25}}{\textbf{36}}$

11.

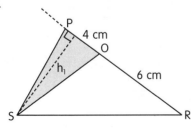

$\dfrac{\text{Area of } \triangle POS}{\text{Area of } \triangle ORS} = \dfrac{\frac{1}{2} \times 4 \times h_1}{\frac{1}{2} \times 6 \times h_1} = \dfrac{2}{3}$

$\dfrac{\text{Area of } \triangle QOR}{\text{Area of } \triangle ORS} = \dfrac{\frac{1}{2} \times 5 \times h_2}{\frac{1}{2} \times 7.5 \times h_2} = \dfrac{2}{3}$

$\dfrac{\text{Area of } \triangle POS}{\text{Area of } \triangle QOR}$

$= \dfrac{\text{Area of } \triangle POS}{\text{Area of } \triangle ORS} \times \dfrac{\text{Area of } \triangle ORS}{\text{Area of } \triangle QOR}$

$= \dfrac{2}{3} \times \dfrac{3}{2} = \dfrac{1}{1} = \textbf{1}$

## 5  Ratio

### Practice Questions (pp. 56–59)

1.  Kate    : Peter
    5      :   6
    6 units → 24 marbles
    1 unit  → 24 ÷ 6 = 4 marbles
    5 units → 5 × 4 = 20 marbles
    Kate has **20** marbles.

2.  Men      :    Women    :    Total
    7      :      4      :   7 + 4 = 11
    Difference between men and women
    = 7 units – 4 units = 3 units
    3 units → 9
    1 unit  → 9 ÷ 3 = 3
    11 units → 11 × 3 = 33
    There are **33** people in the room.

3.  Boys      :    Girls    :    Total
    7      :      5      :   7 + 5 =12
    Difference between boys and girls
    = 7 units – 5 units = 2 units
    12 units → 60 members
    1 unit   → 60 ÷ 12 = 5 members
    2 units  → 2 × 5 = 10 members
    There are **10** more boys than girls.

4.  Mike      :    Doris
    3      :      7
    6      :      14

    Mike

    Doris

    The new ratio of Mike's envelopes to Doris's envelopes is 5 : 15, simplified to **1 : 3**.

5. 
| Esther | : | Andy |
|--------|---|------|
| 5 | : | 8 |
| 10 | : | 16 |

Esther

Andy

The new ratio of Esther's cards to
Andy's cards is **7 : 19**.

6. 
| Daniel | : | Mary | : | Total |
|--------|---|------|---|-------|
| 9 | : | 13 | : | 9 + 13 = 22 |

13 units ⟶ 52 coins
1 unit ⟶ 52 ÷ 13 = 4 coins
22 units ⟶ 22 × 4 = 88 coins
They have **88** coins altogether.

7. 

Oranges ☐☐☐ 18 kg
Pineapples ☐☐☐☐☐☐

3 units ⟶ 18 kg
1 unit ⟶ 18 kg ÷ 3 = 6 kg
11 units ⟶ 11 × 6 kg = 66 kg
Total mass of oranges and pineapples
= 66 kg

apples | oranges and pineapples

66 kg

6 units ⟶ 66 kg
1 unit ⟶ 66 kg ÷ 6 = 11 kg
11 units ⟶ 11 × 11 kg = 121 kg
Total mass of the fruits = **121 kg**

8. Tim's current age
= 25 years + 10 years
= 35 years

| | Jay | : | Tim | : | Angela |
|--|-----|---|-----|---|--------|
| | 3 | : | 7 | : | 9 |
| Current age | 15 | : | 35 | : | 45 |
| 5 years' time | 20 | : | 40 | : | 50 |
| | **2** | : | **4** | : | **5** |

9. 

$75

Joyce

Leslie

1 unit

$48

3 units ⟶ $75 − $48 = $27
1 unit ⟶ $27 ÷ 3 = $9
7 units ⟶ 7 × $9 = $63
4 units ⟶ 4 × $9 = $36
Amount of money Joyce had left = **$63**
Amount of money Leslie had left = **$36**

**Challenging Problems** (pp. 62–66)

1. 
*Before*

Terry

Maria

*After*

Terry       $20

Maria

5 units ⟶ $20
1 unit ⟶ $20 ÷ 5 = $4
4 units ⟶ 4 × $4 = $16
Terry had **$16** at first.

2. *Method 1*
*Before*

Michael

Janet

*After*

24

Michael

Janet

6 units ⟶ 24
1 unit ⟶ 24 ÷ 6 = 4
4 units ⟶ 4 × 4 = 16
Number of books Michael had at first = **16**

*Method 2*

| | Michael | : | Janet |
|--|---------|---|-------|
| + 24 books | 4 | : | 5 |
| | 10 | : | 5 |

10 units − 4 units = 24 books
6 units = 24
1 unit = 24 ÷ 6 = 4
4 units = 4 × 4 = 16
Number of books Michael had at first = **16**

3. *Before*

Adrian

Susan

*After*

Adrian

Susan

21

7 units ⟶ 21
1 unit ⟶ 21 ÷ 7 = 3
6 units ⟶ 6 × 3 = 18
Number of crayons Adrian had at first = **18**

4. *Before*

Elaine

Lynn

*After*

Elaine

Lynn

3 units → $15
1 unit → $15 ÷ 3 = $5
10 units → 10 × $5 = $50
Amount of money Elaine had at first = **$50**

5. Boys

Girls

7 units → 216 − 48 = 168
1 unit → 168 ÷ 7 = 24
6 units → 6 × 24 = 144
Number of boys who wore glasses at first
= **144**

6. Joe

Fred

given to Fred

15

Number of units Joe gave to Fred = 5
5 units → 15
1 unit → 15 ÷ 5 = 3
16 units → 16 × 3 = 48
Number of marbles Joe had at first = **48**

7. *Before*

Men : Women
17 : 15

*After*
9 units

Men : Women    8 units
8 : 7

9 units → 90 men
1 unit → 10 men
8 units → 80 women
1 unit → 10 women
Total number of units at first = 17 + 15 = 32
Total number of people who registered
= 32 × 10
= **320**

8. Number of boys : Number of girls
2 : 3
14 : 21
Number of girls : Number of teachers
7 : 4
21 : 12
Number : Number : Number
of boys   of girls   of teachers
14 : 21 : 12

Number of units representing students
14 + 21 = 35
Number of students : Number of teachers
**35** : **12**

9. David : Tom
4 : 5
Tom : Jack
7 : 8
David : Tom : Jack
28 : 35 : 40
Number of units Jack has more than David
= 40 − 28 = 12
12 units → 24
1 unit → 24 ÷ 12 = 2
35 units → 35 × 2 = 70
Number of cards Tom has = **70**

10. Weight : Gold coins : Silver coins
1 : 5 : 4
10 : 50 : 40
4 : 20 : 16
6 : 30 : 24

10 weights can balance either 50 gold coins
or 40 silver coins. Since only 20 gold coins
are used, the mass of 30 gold coins is to
be used by the silver coins.
Total number of silver coins required = **24**

# 6 Decimals

## Practice Questions (pp. 70–73)

1. (a) $157.14 \div 0.00324$

$$= \frac{15.714 \times 10}{3.24 \times 0.001}$$

$$= \frac{15.714}{3.24} \times \frac{10}{0.001}$$

$$= 4.85 \times 10,000$$

$$= \mathbf{48,500}$$

(b) $0.015714 \div 485$

$$= \frac{15.714 \times 0.001}{4.85 \times 100}$$

$$= \frac{15.714}{4.85} \times \frac{0.001}{100}$$

$$= 3.24 \times 0.001$$

$$= \mathbf{0.0000324}$$

(c) $0.0324 \times 4,850$

$$= 3.24 \times 0.01 \times 4.85 \times 1,000$$

$$= 3.24 \times 4.85 \times 0.01 \times 1,000$$

$$= 15.714 \times 10$$

$$= \mathbf{157.14}$$

2. Volume of mixture
= 0.125 L + 0.375 L + 0.25 L
= **0.75 L**

3. Amount of change received
= $100 − $74.95 − $23.50
= **$1.55**

4. Amount spent = 7 × $1.32
$\qquad$= $9.24
Amount of change received
= $20 − $9.24 = **$10.76**

5. Number of days needed = 6 ÷ 0.4
$$= \frac{6 \times 10}{0.4 \times 10}$$
$$= \frac{60}{4}$$
$$= \mathbf{15}$$

6. Fraction needed = $0.45 ÷ $1.35
$$= \frac{0.45 \times 100}{1.35 \times 100}$$
$$= \frac{45}{135}$$
$$= \frac{1}{3}$$
You can buy $\frac{1}{3}$ **kg** of grapes with $0.45.

7. Cost of 8 notebooks = 8 × $2.45 = $19.60
Cost of 8 files = 8 × $4.25 = $34
Cost of 8 watches = 8 × $14.95 = $119.60
Cost of 9 balls = 9 × $12.50 = $112.50
Total amount spent
= $19.60 + $34 + $119.60 + $112.50
= **$285.70**

8. 1.52 m − 1.23 m = 0.29 m
Alex is 0.29 m taller than Cathy.
Denise's height = 1.23 m − 0.29 m
$\qquad$= **0.94 m**

9.
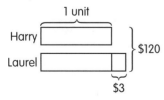
$1,200

cell phone　helmet　money left

10 − 4 = 6 units
0.5 × 6 = 3 units
10 units ⟶ $1,200
1 unit ⟶ $1,200 ÷ 10 = $120
3 units ⟶ 3 × $120 = $360
Amount of money Roger had left = **$360**

10. Amount of money Laurel earned more than
Harry = $0.60 × 5 = $3

1 unit

Harry 〔　　　　〕 ⎱ $120
Laurel 〔　　　　　〕 ⎰
$3

2 units ⟶ $120 − $3 = $117
1 unit ⟶ $117 ÷ 2 = $58.50
Amount of money Laurel earned per hour
= ($58.50 ÷ 5) + $0.60 = **$12.30**

11.
6.25 kg

Bag A

Bag B

1.4 kg

0.35 kg
2 units ⟶ 6.25 kg − 1.4 kg − 0.35 kg
$\qquad$= 4.5 kg
1 unit ⟶ 4.5 kg ÷ 2 = 2.25 kg
New mass of sand in Bag B
= 2.25 kg − 1.4 kg = **0.85 kg**

**Challenging Problems** (pp. 76–80)

1. Work backwards.
Let the number be ▲.
23.69 − 10 = 13.69
Then ▲ × ▲ = 13.69.
13.69 = 1369 × 0.01
$\qquad$= 37 × 37 × 0.01
$\qquad$= 37 × 0.1 × 37 × 0.1
$\qquad$= 3.7 × 3.7
Hence, the number is **3.7**.

2. Notice that the pattern of 6 digits, 053410,
repeats itself in the same order.
50 = 6 × 8 + 2
Since 50 is 2 more than 48, which is a
multiple of 6, the 50th digit will be the 2nd
digit after the digit 2. The 50th digit is **5**.

3. $\frac{3}{7}$ = 0.428571 428571…

21 = 3 × 6 + 3
Since 21 is 3 more than 18, which is a
multiple of 6, the 21st digit will be the digit
wgich is 3 places to the right of 1. The 21st
digit is **8**.

4. $1 + $0.50 + $0.20 + $0.10 + $0.05 = $1.85
Number of coins for each denomination
= $42.55 ÷ $1.85 = 23
Total number of coins = 23 × 5 = **115**

5. *Method 1*

A slice of cake 〔　　　　〕

A pie 〔　〕

15 pies ⟶ 15 × 2 = 30 units
7 slices of cake ⟶ 7 × 5 = 35 units
30 + 35 = 65 units ⟶ $55.25
1 unit ⟶ $55.25 ÷ 65 = $0.85
Cost of 1 pie = 2 × $0.85 = $1.70
Cost of 2 slices of cake = 10 × $0.85
$\qquad$= $8.50
Total cost of 1 pie and 2 slices of cake
= $1.70 + $8.50 = **$10.20**

*Method 2*

1 pie costs as much as $\frac{2}{5}$ of a slice of cake.

15 pies cost as much as $\frac{2}{5} \times 15 = 6$ slices of cake.

15 pies + 7 slices of cake
= 6 slices of cake + 7 slices of cake
13 slices of cake ⟶ $55.25
1 slice of cake ⟶ $55.25 ÷ 13 = $4.25
1 pie ⟶ $\frac{2}{5} \times$ $4.25 = $1.70

Total cost of 1 pie and 2 slices of cake
= $1.70 + 2 × $4.25 = **$10.20**

6. 

| R | T | S | T |
|---|---|---|---|

$\underbrace{\phantom{xxxxxx}}$ 69.95 kg   63.10 kg

Total mass of Robbie, Sarah, and two trophies = 69.95 kg + 63.10 kg = 133.05 kg
(a) Mass of 1 trophy
    = (133.05 kg − 116.05 kg) ÷ 2 = **8.5 kg**
(b) Robbie's mass = 69.95 kg − 8.5 kg
    = **61.45 kg**
(c) Sarah's mass = 63.10 kg − 8.5 kg
    = **54.6 kg**

7. Tank A   [ 0.45 ]

Tank B   [ 0.45 ][ 0.45 ][ 0.45 ][ 0.45 ][ 0.45 ]

2 units ⟶ 12.75 L − (0.45 L × 5) = 10.5 L
1 unit ⟶ 10.5 L ÷ 2 = 5.25 L
3 units ⟶ 3 × 5.25 L = 15.75 L
Initial volume of water in Tank B = **15.75 L**

8. Day 1   [ ]

Day 2   [ $1.40 ]

Day 3   [ $1.40 ][ $1.40 ]

Day 4   [ $1.40 ][ $1.40 ][ $1.40 ]

Day 5   [ $1.40 ][ $1.40 ][ $1.40 ][ $1.40 ]

Day 6   [ $1.40 ][ $1.40 ][ $1.40 ][ $1.40 ][ $1.40 ]

Day 7   [ $1.40 ][ $1.40 ][ $1.40 ][ $1.40 ][ $1.40 ][ $1.40 ]

7 units ⟶ $36.40 − (21 × $1.40) = $7
1 unit ⟶ $7 ÷ 7 = $1
His savings on the third day
= $1 + $1.40 + $1.40
= **$3.80**

9. 

Paul
Ian
Calvin

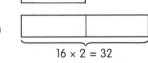

$\frac{2}{3}$ of Ian's money ⟶ 7 units

$\frac{3}{3}$ of Ian's money ⟶ $\frac{7}{2} \times 3 = \frac{21}{2}$ units

$\frac{21}{2} + 7 = \frac{35}{2}$ units ⟶ $63

1 unit ⟶ $63 × $\frac{2}{35}$ = $3.60
10 units ⟶ 10 × $3.60 = $36
Amount of money Paul had at first = **$36**

10. Amount of money the company would receive if all the plates were not broken
= 78 × $1.50 = $117
Amount of money that the company lost
= $117 − $73 = $44
Amount of money the shop owner would save on each broken plate = $1.50 + $9.50
= $11
Number of broken plates = $44 ÷ $11 = **4**

11. $0.45 = \frac{45}{100} = \frac{9}{20}$

$N \times \frac{9}{20}$ = a whole number

We look for a whole number, which is a multiple of 20, between 35 and 45.
The only number $N$ can be is **40**.

# 7 Volume

**Practice Questions** (pp. 83-87)

1. Required length
$= \frac{1}{4} \div \frac{2}{3} \div \frac{1}{2}$
$= \frac{1}{4} \times \frac{3}{2} \times \frac{2}{1}$
$= \frac{1 \times 3 \times 2}{4 \times 2 \times 1}$
$= \frac{6}{8}$
$= \frac{3}{4}$ **m**

2. 

16

Width   [        ]

Length   [        |        ]

16 × 2 = 32

Height   [ ]

$\frac{1}{4} \times 16 = 4$

Volume of block
= length × width × height
= 32 cm × 16 cm × 3 cm
= **2,048 cm³**

3. Increase in height of water level
   = 10.8 m – 7 m = 3.8 m
   Volume of water added
   = Length × width × height
   = 22 m × 18 m × 3.8 m
   = **1,504.8 m³**

4. Height of water level to be filled
   = 22 cm – 18 cm = 4 cm
   Volume of water to fill the tank
   = 36 cm × 24 cm × 4 cm
   = 3,456 cm³
   = 3,000 cm³ + 456 cm³
   = 3 L + 456 mL
   = **3 L 456 mL**

5. Fraction of container to be filled
   $= 1 - \dfrac{3}{5} = \dfrac{2}{5}$
   Volume of water needed to fill the tank completely
   $= \dfrac{2}{5} \times 38$ cm × 30 cm × 18 cm
   = 8,208 cm³
   = **8 L 208 mL**

6. The block has 8 corners.
   Volume of 8 cubes
   = 8 × (4 cm × 4 cm × 4 cm) = 512 cm³
   Volume of remaining block
   = (48 cm × 36 cm × 28 cm) – 512 cm³
   = **47,872 cm³**

7. Volume of water in the tank
   = 60 cm × 55 cm × 35 cm = 115,500 cm³
   29.7 L = 29,700 mL = 29,700 cm³
   Volume of water left in the tank
   = 115,500 cm³ – 29,700 cm³ = 85,800 cm³
   New height of water level $= \dfrac{85,800}{60 \times 55}$
   = **26 cm**

8.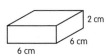
   (a) Volume of box = 8 cm × 8 cm × 1 cm
       = **64 cm³**

   (b) Volume of box = 6 cm × 6 cm × 2 cm
       = **72 cm³**

   (c) Volume of box = 4 cm × 4 cm × 3 cm
       = **48 cm³**

9.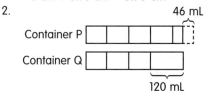
   6 units ⟶ 522 L – 30 L = 492 L
   1 unit ⟶ 492 L ÷ 6 = 82 L
   Capacity of Tank P = 82 L + 30 L = **112 L**

10. Volume of water
    = (20 cm × 9 cm × 8 cm) + [(20 – 12) cm × 9 cm × (10 – 8) cm]
    = **1,584 cm³**

## Challenging Problems (pp. 90–94)

1. Original height of water level $= \dfrac{2}{3} \times 12$ cm
   = 8 cm
   Increase in the height of water level
   $= \dfrac{240 \text{ cm}^3}{20 \text{ cm} \times 16 \text{ cm}} = 0.75$ cm
   New height of water level
   = 8 cm + 0.75 cm = **8.75 cm**

2. 
   2 units ⟶ 46 mL + 120 mL = 166 mL
   1 unit ⟶ 166 mL ÷ 2 = 83 mL
   5 units ⟶ 5 × 83 mL = 415 mL
   Volume of water in Container P at first
   = **415 mL**

3. $\dfrac{2}{3}$ of the tank ⟶ 50 L
   $\dfrac{1}{3}$ of the tank ⟶ 50 L ÷ 2 = 25 L
   25 L = 25,000 cm³
   Height of water level at first
   $= \dfrac{25,000 \text{ cm}^3}{80 \text{ cm} \times 25 \text{ cm}}$
   = **12.5 cm**

4. Fraction of the tank filled with 30 L of water
   $= \dfrac{4}{5} - \dfrac{2}{3} = \dfrac{2}{15}$
   $\dfrac{2}{15}$ of the tank ⟶ 30 L
   $\dfrac{1}{15}$ of the tank ⟶ 30 L ÷ 2 = 15 L
   $\dfrac{4}{5} = \dfrac{12}{15}$
   $\dfrac{12}{15}$ of the tank ⟶ 12 × 15 L = 180 L
   180 L = 180,000 cm³

Height of the water level at first

$$= \frac{180{,}000 \text{ cm}^3}{90 \text{ cm} \times 25 \text{ cm}}$$

= **80 cm**

5. Fraction of tank filled by 6 pails of water

$$= \frac{4}{5} - \frac{1}{2} = \frac{3}{10}$$

Volume of water in 6 pails

$$= \frac{3}{10} \times (120 \text{ cm} \times 100 \text{ cm} \times 80 \text{ cm})$$

= 288,000 cm³

Capacity of each pail = 288,000 cm³ ÷ 6

= 48,000 cm³

= **48,000 mL**

6. Volume of metal cube = 7 cm × 7 cm × 7 cm

= 343 cm³

343 cm³ = 343 mL

Amount of additional water that the container could hold

= 5,500 mL – 2,145 mL – 343 mL

= 3,012 mL

= **3 L 12 mL**

7. Volume of 12 metal cubes

= 2,000 cm³ + 264 cm³ – 764 cm³

= 1,500 cm³

Volume of 1 metal cube = 1,500 cm³ ÷ 12

= 125 cm³

125 cm² = 5 cm × 5 cm × 5 cm

Length of each metal cube = **5 cm**

8. Capacity of 1 glass = Capacity of 2 cups

Capacity of 4 glasses = Capacity of 8 cups

Capacity of 4 glasses and 7 cups

= Capacity of 15 cups

$\frac{3}{5}$ of the water ⟶ 15 cups

$\frac{1}{5}$ of the water ⟶ 15 ÷ 3 = 5 cups

$\frac{2}{5}$ of the water ⟶ 2 × 5 = 10 cups

Number of cups she could fill = **10**

9. Capacity of container

12 bottles   6 bottles + 5 glasses

5 units ⟶ 12 bottles

$2\frac{1}{2}$ units ⟶ 12 ÷ 2 = 6 bottles

$\frac{1}{2}$ unit ⟶ 5 glasses

1 unit ⟶ 2 × 5 = 10 glasses

8 units ⟶ 8 × 10 = 80 glasses

Number of glasses = **80**

10. Note that 14 is a multiple of 7 and 15 is a multiple of 5, but 16 is not a multiple of 3. The nearest multiple of 3 from 16 is 15. Maximum number of blocks

$$= \frac{14 \times 15 \times 15}{7 \times 5 \times 3} = \textbf{30}$$

## 8 Percentage

### Practice Questions (pp. 98–100)

1. 75% $= \frac{75}{100} = \frac{3}{4}$

Number of students who passed the exam

$= \frac{3}{4} \times 48 = \textbf{36}$

2. If Albert received 60%, then Anthony received 100% – 60% = 40%.

Difference = 60% – 40% = 20%

Difference in votes = 20% × 30

$= \frac{20}{100} \times 30$

= 6

Albert received **6** more votes.

3. *Method 1*

Percentage profit on 10 phones

= Percentage profit on 1 phone

Hence, percentage profit on 1 phone is **20%**.

*Method 2*

Suppose the owner bought 10 similar phones for $1,000 and sold them for $1,200, making a profit of $200, or 20%.

Hence each phone cost $100 and was sold for $120, making a profit of $20 each. He made a percentage profit of

$\frac{\$20}{\$100} \times 100\% = \textbf{20\%}$ for each phone.

4. Percentage of amount paid

= 100% – 30% = 70%

70% ⟶ $119.

1% ⟶ $119 ÷ 70 = $1.70

100% ⟶ $1.70 × 100 = $170

The original price of the watch was **$170**.

5.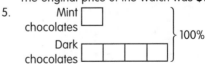

Mint chocolates

Dark chocolates

100%

5 units ⟶ 100%

1 unit ⟶ 100% ÷ 5 = 20%

Percentage of mint chocolates = **20%**

6. Number of whole numbers from 4 to 23: 20

Numbers in multiples of 5 from 4 to 23:

5, 10, 15, and 20

Percentage $= \frac{4}{20} \times 100\% = \textbf{20\%}$

7. Number of boys who received prizes
= 20% × 50 = 10
Number of girls who received prizes
= 30% × 30 = 9
Total number of contestants who received
prizes = 10 + 9
= 19
Total number of contestants = 50 + 30
= 80
Percentage of contestants who received

prizes = $\frac{19}{80}$ × 100% = **23.75%**

8. Initial price of watch ⟶ 100%
Price after 10% discount ⟶ 90%
Price after increasing the discounted price

by 5% = $\frac{105}{100}$ × 90% = 94.5%

New percentage discount

= $\frac{100\% - 94.5\%}{100\%}$ × 100% = **5.5%**

9.
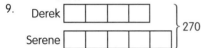

Derek | | | | |
Serene | | | | | | } 270

9 units ⟶ 270
1 unit ⟶ 270 ÷ 9 = 30
4 units ⟶ 4 × 30 = 120
Number of stickers Derek has = **120**

## Challenging Problems (pp. 103–106)

1. Buying price of the first TV set

= $\frac{\$6,000}{120\%}$ × 100% = $5,000

Buying price of the second TV set

= $\frac{\$6,000}{80\%}$ × 100% = $7,500

Amount Jonathan spent on the two TV sets
= $5,000 + $7,500 = $12,500
Amount he received for the two TV sets
= $6,000 × 2 = $12,000
So, he had a total loss of $12,500 – $12,000
= **$500**

2. New length of rectangle
= 120% × length
= 1.2 length
New width of rectangle
= 120% × width
= 1.2 width
New area of rectangle
= new length × new width
= 1.2 length × 1.2 width
= (1.2 × 1.2) area
= 1.44 area
New area expressed as percentage
= 1.44 × 100% = 144%
Percentage increase in area
= 144% – 100% = **44%**

3. New length or width of square
= 130% of length or width
= 1.3 length or 1.3 width
New area = new length × new width
= 1.3 length × 1.3 width
= (1.3 × 1.3) area
= 1.69 area
New area expressed as percentage
= 1.69 × 100% = 169%
Percentage increase in area
= 169% – 100%= **69%**

4. Suppose Jack and Jill had $100 at first.

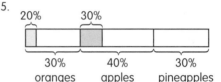

| | Jack | Jill |
|---|---|---|
| **6 months later** | 110% x $100 = $110 | 90% x $100 = $90 |
| **1 year later** | 90% x $110 = $99 | 110% x $90 = $99 |

**Both** had the same amount of money in the end.

5.
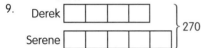

20%        30%

30%        40%        30%
oranges    apples     pineapples

Let the number of fruits be 100.
Number of oranges = 30% × 100
= 30
Number of rotten oranges = 20% × 30
= 6
Number of apples = 40% × 100
= 40
Number of rotten apples = 30% × 40
= 12
Number of fruits that are in good condition
= 100 – 6 – 12
= 82
Percentage of fruits that are in good

condition = $\frac{82}{100}$ × 100% = **82%**

6. <u>Before</u>

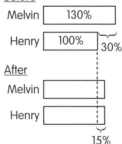

Melvin | 130% |
Henry | 100% | } 30%

<u>After</u>

Melvin | |
Henry | |

15%

15% of the marbles ⟶ 30
1% of the marbles ⟶ 30 ÷ 15 = 2
100% of the marbles ⟶ 100 × 2 = 200
Number of marbles Henry has = **200**

7. 60% of Mike's candies ⟶ 24

100% of Mike's candies ⟶ $\frac{24}{60} \times 100 = 40$

*Before*

Mike | 40 |

Bobby | 66 |

*After*

Mike | 40 | ? |

Bobby | |

Difference in the number of candies
= 66 − 40 = 26
Number of candies Bobby must give to
Mike = 26 ÷ 2
= **13**

8. Number of Singapore coins
= 60% × 400 = 240
Number of Malaysia coins
= 400 − 240 = 160
32% of coins ⟶ 160
100% of coins ⟶ 500
Number of Singapore coins he bought
= 500 − 400 = **100**

9. Number of Indonesia stamps = 35% × 400
= 140
Number of Malaysia stamps = 65% × 400
= 260
After 100 stamps were added,
Total number of stamps = 400 + 100
= 500
Number of Malaysia stamps = 70% × 500
= 350
Number of Malaysia stamps added
= 350 − 260 = 90
Number of Indonesia stamps added
= 100 − 90 = **10**

10. $\frac{25}{100} \times$ Number A = 125

Number A = $125 \times \frac{100}{25} = 500$

$\frac{0.35}{100} \times$ Number B = 10.5

Number B = $10.5 \times \frac{100}{0.35}$

= 3,000
Sum = 500 + 3,000 = **3,500**

## 9 Angles and Triangles

### Practice Questions (pp.110–113)

1. Since RS is a straight line,
m∠y = 180° − 128° = **52°**.
Since PQ is a straight line,
m∠x = 180° − 52° − 42° = **86°**

2. Sum of angles at a point is 360°,
m∠x = 360° − 26° − 90° − 32° − 94°
= **118°**

3. Let the point of intersection be O.
Then m∠ROT = m∠UOS = 103°.
m∠x = 180° − 103° − 42° = **35°**

4. 2(m∠z) = 180° − 110° − 28°
= 42°
m∠z = 42° ÷ 2
= **21°**

5. 3(m∠q) = 360° − 68° − 130°
= 162°
m∠q = 162° ÷ 3
= **54°**

6. m∠x = 5(m∠y)
5(m∠y) + m∠y = 360° − 61° − 37° − 40°
6(m∠y) = 222°
m∠y = 222° ÷ 6
= **37°**
m∠x = 5 × 37° = **185°**

7. Since PQ = RQ, triangle PQR is an isosceles
triangle, ∠P = ∠R.
m∠P + m∠R = 180° − 76°
2(m∠P) = 104°
m∠P = 104° ÷ 2 = 52°
Hence, ∠QPR = **52°** and ∠PRQ = **52°**.

8. Since △ABC is an equilateral triangle,
m∠A = m∠B = ∠C = 60°.
Since AE = AD, △ADE is an isosceles triangle,
m∠D = m∠E.
m∠ADE = $\frac{180° − 60°}{2}$ = **60°**

9. Since PR = QR, △PQR is an isosceles triangle,
m∠P = m∠Q.
m∠PQR = (180° − 68°) ÷ 2 = 56°
m∠PQS = 56° − 34° = **22°**

10.

m∠EDC = 180° − 83° = 97°
m∠DEC = 180° − 97° − 37° = 46°
m∠p = 180° − m∠DEC
= 180° − 46°
= **134°**

11. **68°**

## Challenging Problems (pp. 115–118)

1.  $m\angle PTQ = 180° - 52°$
    $= 128°$
    $m\angle a = (180° - 128°) \div 2$
    $= \mathbf{26°}$
    $m\angle PTS = 180° - 90° - 26°$
    $= 64°$
    $m\angle b = 52° + 64°$
    $= \mathbf{116°}$
2.  $m\angle PRQ = 180° - 90° - 68°$
    $= 22°$
    $m\angle TRS = 60°$
    $m\angle z = 180° - 22° - 60°$
    $= \mathbf{98°}$
3.  $m\angle PSX = 180° - 90° - 62°$
    $= 28°$
    $m\angle XSY = 90° - 28°$
    $= 62°$
    $m\angle XYS = 180° - 111°$
    $= 69°$
    $m\angle a = 180° - 62° - 69°$
    $= \mathbf{49°}$
4.  $m\angle PQO = 64°$
    $m\angle YAP = \angle QPO$
    $= 180° - 64° - 52°$
    $= \mathbf{64°}$
5.  *Method 1*
    $m\angle VXW = 180° - 90° - 73°$
    $= 17°$
    $m\angle YZX = (180° - 90°) \div 2$
    $= 45°$
    $m\angle p = 17° + 45°$
    $= \mathbf{62°}$
    *Method 2*
    $m\angle VXW = 180° - 90° - 73°$
    $= 17°$
    $m\angle YXU = 90° - 17°$
    $= 73°$
    $m\angle p = 180° - 45° - 73°$
    $= \mathbf{62°}$
6.  $m\angle QRS = 60°$
    $m\angle QRP = (180° - 28°) \div 2$
    $= 76°$
    $m\angle y = 76° - 60°$
    $= \mathbf{16°}$
7.  $m\angle TPQ = 180° - 90° - 17°$
    $= 73°$
    $m\angle TPR = 73° - 32°$
    $= 41°$
    $m\angle STP = \angle SPT = 41°$
    $m\angle y = 180° - (2 \times 41°)$
    $= \mathbf{98°}$

8.  Since the sum of the angles in a triangle is 180°,
    $m\angle a + m\angle c + m\angle e = 180°$
    $m\angle b + m\angle d + m\angle f = 180°$
    $m\angle a + m\angle b + m\angle c + m\angle d + m\angle e + m\angle f$
    $= 180° + 180°$
    $= \mathbf{360°}$

# 10 Quadrilaterals

## Practice Questions (pp. 122–125)

1.  Since AB is parallel to DC, and angles between two parallel lines sum to 180°,
    $m\angle p = 180° - 25° - 130° = \mathbf{25°}$.
2.  Since AD is parallel to BC, and angles between two parallel lines sum to 180°,
    $m\angle CBD = 180° - 27° - 78° = \mathbf{75°}$.
3.  Since the opposite angles of a parallelogram are equal, $m\angle y = m\angle RSP$.
    In $\triangle PRS$, $m\angle RSP = 180° - 54° - 75°$
    $= 51°$
    Hence, $m\angle y = \mathbf{51°}$.
4.  Since the opposite angles of a parallelogram are equal,
    $m\angle QRS = m\angle SPQ = 116°$
    In $\triangle QRS$, $m\angle SQR = 180° - 24° - 116°$
    $= \mathbf{40°}$
5.  Since each pair of angles between two parallel sides add up to 180°,
    $m\angle BCD = 180° - 106° = \mathbf{74°}$.
    Likewise, for $m\angle DAB$, $m\angle DAB = \mathbf{74°}$.
    Since opposite angles of a parallelogram are equal, $m\angle ABC = m\angle ADC = \mathbf{106°}$.
    Note: There are at least two ways to find out each unknown angle.
6.  A rhombus is a special kind of parallelogram.
    $m\angle ABC = 180° - 68° = \mathbf{112°}$
    $m\angle BCD = m\angle BAD = \mathbf{68°}$
    $m\angle CDA = m\angle ABC = \mathbf{112°}$
7.  A rhombus is a parallelogram with all sides equal.
    Since HE = HG, $\triangle EGH$ is an isosceles triangle, $m\angle HGE = m\angle HEG = 64°$.
    $m\angle x = m\angle EHG$
    $= 180° - 64° - 64°$
    $= \mathbf{52°}$
8.  $m\angle RSP = 180° - 110°$
    $= 70°$
    $m\angle PST = \angle PSR - 28°$
    $= 70° - 28°$
    $= \mathbf{42°}$

9. $m\angle RQS = (180° - 62°) \div 2$
$= 59°$
$m\angle PQS = 180° - 59°$
$= 121°$
$m\angle x = \textbf{121°}$
$m\angle y = 180° - 121°$
$= \textbf{59°}$
10. $m\angle BED = 180° - 130°$
$= 50°$
$m\angle EAD = \angle EDA = 50° \div 2$
$= 25°$
$m\angle ADC = 25° + 130°$
$= \textbf{155°}$

## Challenging Problems (pp. 127–131)

1. $m\angle IHF = 180° - 89°$
$= 91°$
$m\angle GHF = 180° - 91°$
$= 89°$
$m\angle FGH = 180° - 89° \div 2$
$= \textbf{45.5°}$
Note: We cannot assume that parallelogram EFHI is a
rectangle, or $\angle IHF = 90°$.
2. $m\angle LPM = m\angle LMP$
$= (180° - 90°) \div 2$
$= 45°$
$m\angle KPN = 180° - 90° - 28°$
$= 62°$
$m\angle NPM = 180° - 62° - 45°$
$= \textbf{73°}$
3. $m\angle PRS = 180° - 42° - 74°$
$= 64°$
$m\angle RPQ = 180° - 42° - 74°$
$= 64°$
$m\angle QRP = 180° - 64° - 64°$
$= 52°$
$m\angle SRQ = 52° + 64°$
$= \textbf{116°}$
4. $m\angle ABE = 180° - 90° - 42°$
$= 48°$
$m\angle DBC = 180° - 90° - 58°$
$= 32°$
$m\angle EBD = 90° - 48° - 32°$
$= \textbf{10°}$
5. $m\angle SRQ = 180° - 56° - 62°$
$= 62°$
$m\angle RQS = 56°$
$m\angle PQS = 180° - 56° - 62°$
$= \textbf{62°}$
6. $m\angle ABS = \angle SAB$
$= (180° - 90°) \div 2$
$= 45°$
$m\angle RBC = 60°$
$m\angle ABC = 180° - 45° - 60°$
$= \textbf{75°}$

7. $m\angle PSQ = m\angle PQS = 40°$
$m\angle QPS = 180° - (2 \times 40°)$
$= 100°$
$m\angle RST = 180° - 100° - 40°$
$= 40°$
$m\angle QTR = 40° + 42°$
$= \textbf{82°}$
8. $m\angle BQR = 180° - 105°$
$= 75°$
$m\angle DCB = 90°$
$m\angle BCQ = 180° - 90° - 38°$
$= 52°$
$m\angle CBQ = 180° - 52° - 75°$
$= \textbf{53°}$
9. $m\angle CBE = 180° - 63° - 63°$
$= 54°$
$m\angle BCD = 180° - 63°$
$= 117°$
$m\angle BAE = 117° - 90°$
$= \textbf{27°}$
$m\angle ABC = 180° - 117°$
$= 63°$
$m\angle BEA = 180° - 27° - 63° - 54°$
$= \textbf{36°}$
10. $m\angle ABE = m\angle DCE = 60° + 90°$
$= 150°$
$m\angle BEA = m\angle EAB = (180° - 150°) \div 2$
$= 15°$
$m\angle CDE = m\angle DEC = (180° - 150°) \div 2$
$= 15°$
$m\angle x = 60° - 15° - 15°$
$= \textbf{30°}$

## 11 Average and Plots

### Practice Questions (pp. 134–140)

1. The six 3-digit numbers are: 237, 273, 327, 372, 723, and 732
Sum of numbers
$= 237 + 273 + 327 + 372 + 723 + 732$
$= 2,664$
Average $= 2,664 \div 6$
$= \textbf{444}$
2. Total score for the 5 tests
$= 18 \times 5 = 90$ points
Total score for the 6 tests
$= 90 + 24 = 114$ points
Lynette's average score for all six tests
$= 114 \div 6 = \textbf{19 points}$.
3. Total score for Robin's first three tests
$= 64 \times 3 = 192$ points
In the 4th test, Robin scored
$64 + 28 = 92$ points
Total score for the four tests
$= 192 + 92 = 284$ points
Robin's new average score
$= 284 \div 4 = \textbf{71 points}$

4. Total value of the 5 numbers = 7 × 5 = 35
   Total value of the 4 remaining numbers
   = 6 × 4 = 24
   The value of the number that was removed
   is 35 − 24 = **11**.
5. Total score of Sean and Ted
   = 68 × 2 = 136 points
   Total score of Sean, Ted, and Mary
   = 72 × 3 = 216 points
   Mary's test score = 216 − 136 = **80 points**.
6. 25 boys + 15 girls = 40 students
   Total score of 40 students
   = 68 × 40 = 2,720 points
   Total score of 25 boys
   = 62 × 25 = 1,550 points
   Total score of 15 girls
   = 2,720 − 1,550 = 1,170 points
   Average score of the 15 girls
   = 1,170 ÷ 15 = **78 points**
7. (a) Total number of paper clips
      = 100 + 150 + 250 = 500
      Total mass of the paper clips
      = 500 × 3.9 g = **1,950 g**
   (b) 2,596 − 1,950 = 646
      The empty box has mass of **646 g**.
8. Total score for Eugene's first three tests
   = 85 × 3 = 255 points
   New average score = 85 + 2 = 87
   Total score for Eugene's four tests
   = 87 × 4 = 348 points
   Eugene must score 348 − 255 = **93 points**
   for the fourth test.
9. 8 tennis player + 7 baseball players
   = 15 players.
   Total mass of 7 baseball players
   = 90 kg × 7 = 630 kg
   Total mass of 15 players
   = 645 kg + 630 kg = 1275 kg
   Average mass of all the players
   = 1275 kg ÷ 15 = **85 kg**
10. Total number of pages read on first three
    days = 61 + 49 + 52 = 162
    Average = 162 ÷ 3 = 54
    Number of pages read on the fourth day
    = 54 + 6
    = **60**
11. (a) 20 × 20¢ = 400¢
          = $4
       16 × 10¢ = 160¢
          = $1.60
       $4 + $1.60 = $5.60
       **Jane** has $5.60 worth of 10¢ and 20¢
       coins.

(b) 16 × 20¢ = 320¢
          = $3.20
    10 × 10¢ = 100¢
          = $1
    $3.20 + $1 = $4.20
    **Lisa** has $4.20 worth of 10¢ and 20¢
    coins.
(c) 8 × 20¢ = 160¢
          = $1.60
    8 × 10¢ = 80¢
    **Fred** has twice as much money in 20¢
    as in 10¢ coins.
(d) 8 × 20¢ = 160¢
          = $1.60
    14 × 10¢ = 140¢
          = $1.40
    $1.60 − $1.40 = 20¢
    **Sue** has 20¢ more in 20¢ coins than in
    10¢ coins.
(e) Ian:
    12 × 20¢ = 240¢
          = $2.40
    16 × 10¢ = 160¢
          = $1.60
    $2.40 + $1.60 = $4
    Paul:
    20 × 20¢ = 400¢
    = $4
    **Ian** and **Paul** have the same amount of
    money.
(f) Sue:
    8 × 20¢ = 160¢
          = $1.60
    14 × 10¢ = 140¢
          = $1.40
    $1.60 + $1.40 = $3
    Lisa:
    16 × 20¢ = 320¢
          = $3.20
    10 × 10¢ = 100¢
          = $1
    $3.20+ $1 = $4.20
    $3 + $4.20 = $7.20
    **Sue** and **Lisa** have a total amount of
    $7.20.

## Challenging Problems (pp. 143–147)

1. Total points scored for 6 tests = 6 × 90
                                    = 540
   If she had scored 100 points on 5 tests, her
   lowest score would be = 540 − (5 × 100)
                          = **40**

2. Sum of the 1,000 whole numbers
= 1 + 2 + 3 + ... + 998 + 999 + 1,000
= (1 + 1,000) + (2 + 999) + ... + (500 + 501)
= $\frac{1,000}{2}$ pairs, where each sum up to 1,001
= 500 × 1,001
Average of the first 1,000 whole numbers
= $\frac{500 \times 1,001}{1,000}$ = **500.5**

3. Total number of customers at first
= 12 × 800 = 9,600
New average = $\frac{9,600}{12 - 4}$
= **1,200**

4.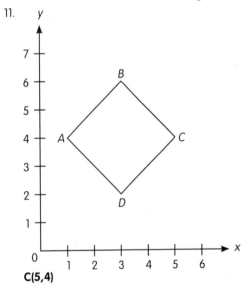

3 units → 453 cm – 8 cm – 19 cm = 426 cm
1 unit → 426 cm ÷ 3 = 142 cm
Esther's height = **142 cm**
Felicia's height = 142 cm + 8 cm = **150 cm**
George's height = 142 cm + 19 cm = **161 cm**

5. Total mass of 5 packages = 5 × 16 kg
= 80 kg
Possible mass of the heaviest package
= 80 kg – 1 kg – 2 kg – 3 kg – 4 kg
= **70 kg**

6. Men : Women : Total
   4  :   5   :  9
Assume that there are 9 adults, hence,
there are 4 men and 5 women.
Total mass = 9 × 72 kg = 648 kg
Total mass of the men = 4 × 82 kg
= 328 kg
Total mass of the women
= 648 kg – 328 kg = 320 kg
Average mass of the women = 320 kg ÷ 5
= **64 kg**

7. Since there are 16 terms, the average
number is between the 8th and 9th terms.
The 8th consecutive odd number is one
less than 122, which is 121. Then we
count backwards to find the smallest odd
number.

| 9th | Average | 8th | 7th | 6th | 5th | 4th | 3rd | 2nd | 1st |
|-----|---------|-----|-----|-----|-----|-----|-----|-----|-----|
| 123 | 122 | 121 | 119 | 117 | 115 | 113 | 111 | 109 | 107 |

The smallest odd number is **107**.

8. Since there are 10 terms, the average
number is between the 5th and 6th terms.
The 6th consecutive odd number is one
more than 100, which is 101. Then we count
forward to find the greatest odd number.

| 1st | 2nd | 3rd | 4th | 5th | Average | 6th | 7th | 8th | 9th | 10th |
|-----|-----|-----|-----|-----|---------|-----|-----|-----|-----|------|
| 91 | 93 | 95 | 97 | 99 | 100 | 101 | 103 | 105 | 107 | 109 |

Sum = 91 + 109 = **200**

9. Total test score of Aaron and Bob = 32
Total test score of Bob and Chris = 36
Total test score of Chris and Dawn = 42
A + B + B + C + C + D = 32 + 36 + 42
A + B + C + B + C + D = 110
   ⏟36      ⏟36
A + D = 110 – 36 – 36 = 38
Average test score of Aaron and Dawn
= 38 ÷ 2 = **19**

10. To change the average score from 76 to 79,
a total of 100 – 79 = 21 points are needed.
Difference in average score = 79 – 76
= 3
Number of tests before the final test
= 21 ÷ 3 = 7
Total number of tests in the year = 7 + 1
= **8**

11.

C(5,4)

# 12 Rate

**Practice Questions** (pp. 150–153)

1. Glenn parked his car for 1 h 40 min.

   9.10 A.M. $\xrightarrow{+ 1 h}$ 10.10 A.M. $\xrightarrow{+ 40\ min}$ 10.50 A.M.

| Time | Charges |
|------|---------|
| First 1 h | $2.80 |
| Next 30 min | $2.20 |
| Last 10 min | $2.20 |
| **Total** | **$7.20** |

2. With water flowing at the same rate,
2 similar taps will halve the time.
So, two taps can fill the tub with water in
$\frac{1}{2}$ × 10 = **5 minutes**.

3. (a) In 15 min, the photocopier can staple 360 booklets.
   In 1 minute, the photocopier can staple $\frac{360}{15}$ = 24 booklets.
   In 20 min, the photocopier can staple 20 × 24 = **480 booklets**.
   (b) The photocopier can staple 24 booklets in 1 minute.
   The photocopier can staple 600 booklets in 600 ÷ 24 = **25 minutes**.

4. Amount needed to charter a bus = $30 × 50 = $1,500
   Each of the 40 students will need to pay $1,500 ÷ 40 = **$37.50**.

5. *Method 1*
   1 h = 60 min
   Sophie runs around the track 8 times in 60 min.
   Sophie runs around the track once in $\frac{60}{8}$ = 7.5 min.
   Since 7.5 min is less than 8 min, **Sophie** runs faster than Ann.
   *Method 2*
   Ann runs around the track once in 8 min.
   Ann runs around the track 8 times in 8 × 8 = 64 min.
   Since 60 min is less than 64 min, **Sophie** is faster.

6. In 1 hour, the machine can produce 53 loaves.
   In 1 day, the machine can produce 24 × 53 = 1,272 loaves.
   In 5 days, the machine can produce 5 × 1,272 = **6,360** loaves.

7.

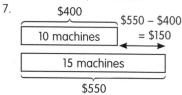

   5 additional machines cost $550 − $400 = $150.
   15 additional machines cost 3 × $150 = $450.
   The rent for 25 machines is $400 + $450 = **$850**.

8.

   6 intervals take 5 seconds.
   1 interval takes $\frac{5}{6}$ seconds.
   From the 10-cm mark to the 1-cm mark, there are 9 intervals.

9 intervals take $\frac{5}{6}$ × 9 = 7.5 seconds.
It will take **7.5 seconds** to reach the 1-cm mark.

9. *Method 1*

| Number of workers | Number of holes | Number of days |
|---|---|---|
| 10 | 20 | 40 |
| 20 | 20 | 40 ÷ 2 = 20 |
| 20 | 10 | 20 ÷ 2 = **10** |

*Method 2*

| Number of workers | Number of holes | Number of days |
|---|---|---|
| 10 | 20 | 40 |
| 10 | 10 | 40 ÷ 2 = 20 |
| 20 | 10 | 20 ÷ 2 = **10** |

10. *Method 1*

| Number of clerks | Number of documents | Number of days |
|---|---|---|
| 3 | 6 | 12 |
| 1 | 6 | 12 × 3 = 36 |
| 2 | 6 | 36 ÷ 2 = 18 |
| 2 | 3 | 18 ÷ 2 = **9** |

*Method 2*

| Number of clerks | Number of documents | Number of days |
|---|---|---|
| 3 | 6 | 12 |
| 3 | 3 | 12 ÷ 2 = 6 |
| 1 | 3 | 6 × 3 = 18 |
| 2 | 3 | 18 ÷ 2 = **9** |

**Challenging Problems** (pp. 155–158)

1. In every hour, Clock B gains an additional 3 min.
   3 min is gained in 1 h.
   60 min is gained in $\frac{1}{3}$ × 60 = 20 h
   Number of hours = **20**

2. In 1 min, cold water flowing from Tap A can fill $\frac{1}{6}$ of the tub.
   In 1 min, hot water flowing from Tap B can fill $\frac{1}{8}$ of the tub.
   In 1 min, water flowing from both taps can fill $\left(\frac{1}{6} + \frac{1}{8}\right) = \frac{7}{24}$ of the tub
   Time taken to fill the tub with water $\left(1 \div \frac{7}{24}\right) = 3\frac{3}{7}$ **min**

3. Cost for 5 guests to stay at the hotel for 7 days = $2,275
   Cost for 3 guests to stay at the hotel for 7 days = ($2,275 ÷ 5) × 3 = $1,365
   Cost for 3 guests to stay at the hotel for 4 days = ($1,365 ÷ 7) × 4 = **$780**

4. Fare for the first two km = $2.80
Fare for the next 17.8 km
= 60 × $0.30
= $18
Total fare = $2.80 + $18
= **$20.80**

5. (a) Total number of travelers = 80 + 16
= 96

Number of days = $\dfrac{12 \times 80}{96}$
= **10**

(b) Total mass of rice = 120 kg + 40 kg
= 160 kg

Number of days = $\dfrac{12 \times 160}{120}$
= 16

Additional number of days = 16 − 12
= **4**

6. *Method 1*

| Number of men | Number of fences | Number of days |
|---|---|---|
| 3 | 5 | 2 |
| 3 | 1 | $\dfrac{2}{5}$ |
| 1 | 1 | $\dfrac{2}{5} \times 3 = \dfrac{6}{5}$ |
| 2 | 1 | $\dfrac{6}{5} \div 2 = \dfrac{3}{5}$ |

*Method 2*

| Number of men | Number of fences | Number of days |
|---|---|---|
| 3 | 5 | 2 |
| 1 | 5 | $2 \times 3 = 6$ |
| 2 | 5 | $6 \div 2 = 3$ |
| 2 | 1 | $3 \times \dfrac{1}{5} = \dfrac{3}{5}$ |

7. *Method 1*

| Number of men | Number of days | Number of boxes |
|---|---|---|
| 6 | 4 | 900 |
| 10 | 4 | $\dfrac{900 \times 10}{6} = 1{,}500$ |
| 10 | 6 | $\dfrac{1{,}500 \times 6}{4} = 2{,}250$ |

*Method 2*

| Number of men | Number of days | Number of boxes |
|---|---|---|
| 6 | 4 | 900 |
| 6 | 6 | $\dfrac{900 \times 6}{4} = 1{,}350$ |
| 10 | 6 | $\dfrac{1{,}350 \times 10}{6} = 2{,}250$ |

8.

| Number of days Aileen takes | Number of days Eve takes | Number of dresses |
|---|---|---|
| 2 | 3 | 48 |
| 4 | 2 | 64 |
| 4 | 6 | $48 \times 2 = 96$ |

In 4 days, Eve can sew 96 − 64
= 32 dresses.
In 1 day, Eve can sew 32 ÷ 4 = 8 dresses.
Number of days Eve will take to sew
48 dresses = 48 ÷ 8 = **6**
In 2 days, Aileen can sew 48 − (3 × 8)
= 24 dresses.
In 1 day, Aileen can sew 24 ÷ 2
= 12 dresses.
Number of days Aileen will take to sew 48
dresses = 48 ÷ 12 = **4**

9.

| Number of days Simon takes | Number of days Lisa takes | Number of houses |
|---|---|---|
| 3 | 1 | $\dfrac{19}{20}$ |
| 4 | 3 | $1\dfrac{3}{5}$ |
| 9 | 3 | $\dfrac{19}{20} \times 3 = 2\dfrac{17}{20}$ |

In 5 days, Simon can paint
$2\dfrac{17}{20} - 1\dfrac{3}{5} = \dfrac{5}{4}$ houses.
In **4** days, Simon can paint 1 house.

In 3 days, Lisa can paint $1\dfrac{3}{5} - 1 = \dfrac{3}{5}$ of
a house.
In **5** days, Lisa can paint 1 house.

10. Since Ben takes 6 days to renovate the
room, he will take 1 day to renovate $\dfrac{1}{6}$ of
the room. Since James takes 15 days to
renovate the room, he will take 1 day to
renovate $\dfrac{1}{15}$ of the room.
Using guess and check,

| Number of days Ben takes | Number of days James takes | Total number of days | Number of rooms renovated |
|---|---|---|---|
| 1 | 8 | 9 | $\dfrac{1}{6} + \left(\dfrac{1}{15} \times 8\right) = \dfrac{7}{10}$ |
| 3 | 6 | 9 | $\left(\dfrac{1}{6} \times 3\right) + \left(\dfrac{1}{15} \times 6\right) = \dfrac{9}{10}$ |
| 4 | 5 | 9 | $\left(\dfrac{1}{6} \times 4\right) + \left(\dfrac{1}{15} \times 5\right) = 1$ |

Number of days Ben will take = **4**

## 13 Data Analysis

### Practice Questions (pp. 162–166)

1. (a) Club D has 110 thousands fans.
   Club E has 290 thousands fans.
   Fraction of fans from club D
   $$= \frac{110}{(110 + 290)} = \frac{11}{40}$$

   (b) Club C has 330,000 fans.
   Number of male fans
   = 330,000 – 150,000 = 180,000
   Number of male : Number of female
   180,000 : 150,000
   **6 : 5**

   (c)
   | Club | Number of fans (in thousands) |
   |------|-------------------------------|
   | A | 270 |
   | B | 200 |
   | C | 330 |
   | D | 110 |
   | E | 290 |

   Average number of fans
   = (270 + 200 + 330 + 110 + 290) ÷ 5
   = 1200 ÷ 5
   = 240 thousands
   = **240,000**

2. (a) Jessie earned $1,200 in February and
   $800 in April.
   Jessie earned $1,200 – $800 = $400 more.

   (b) Jessie earned $600 in January.
   In January, she saved $\frac{2}{5}$ × $600 = $240.
   In February, she saved $\frac{1}{3}$ × $1,200 = $400.
   Jessie saved $240 + $400 = **$640**.

   (c)
   | Month | Earnings |
   |-------|----------|
   | March | $900 |
   | April | $800 |
   | May | $400 |

   Jessie's average earnings from March to
   May = ($900 + $800 + $400) ÷ 3 = **$700**

3. (a) Total number of families
   = 4 + 8 + 7 + 3 + 2 + 1 = **25**

   (b) Number of families with more than
   3 children = 3 + 2 + 1 = 6
   Fraction of the families with more than 3
   children = $\frac{6}{25}$

   (c) Total number of children in the
   neighborhood
   = 1 × 4 + 2 × 8 + 3 × 7 + 4 × 3 + 5 × 2
   + 6 × 1
   = 4 + 16 + 21 + 12 + 10 + 6
   = **69**

4. (a) Number of envelopes that contain less
   than 30 stamps = 8 + 6 = **14**

   (b) Greatest possible number of stamps
   Pauline could have = 40 × 4 = **160**

   (c) Total number of stamps
   = 8 × 10 + 6 × 20 + 10 × 30 + 4 × 40
   + 4 × 50
   = 80 + 120 + 300 + 160 + 200 = **860**

5. (a) Since there are 20 dots, **20** families live
   in the neighborhood.

   (b) Total number of smartphones
   = (2 × 0) + (3 × 1) + (5 × 2) + (6 × 3)
   + (3 × 4) + (1 × 5)
   = 0 + 3 + 10 + 18 + 12 + 5
   = 48
   There are **48** smartphones altogether.

   (c) Out of 20 families, 10 of them have 3 or
   more smartphones per family.
   $$\frac{10}{20} = \frac{1}{2}$$
   $\frac{1}{2}$ of families have 3 or more
   smartphones per family.

### Challenging Problems (pp. 169–170)

1. (a) At 8:20 A.M., the truck had traveled 50
   miles from Town Y.
   Thus, the truck is 80 – 50 = **30 miles**
   from Town X.

   (b) At 8:40 A.M., the car had traveled 50
   miles from Town X, and the truck had
   traveled 55 miles from Town Y.
   Hence, the car is 80 – 50 = **30 miles**
   from Town Y; the truck is 80 – 55
   = **25 miles** from Town X.

   (c) $\frac{3}{4}$ of the journey represents a distance
   of $\frac{3}{4}$ × 80 = 60 miles.

   From the graph, the truck traveled a
   distance of 60 miles at **9:00 A.M.**

2. (a) The highest (lighter) bar represents the
   most popular topic.
   On the graph, **data analysis** was the
   most popular among the students.

   (b) The highest (darker) bar represents the
   least popular topic.
   From the graph, **algebra** was the least
   popular topic among the students.

   (c) Number of students who chose algebra
   as their least favorite topic = 92
   Number of students who chose geometry
   as their least favorite topic = 64
   Total number of students who chose
   algebra and geometry as their least
   favorite topic = 92 + 64 = **156**

(d) From the graph, geometry represents the second highest bar among the 4 favorite topics.
So, **geometry** had the second highest number of students who liked it.

## 14 Review Questions

**Practice Questions** (pp. 172–176)

1.
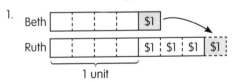
Beth

Ruth

1 unit

From the model,
1 unit → $4
Beth had $4 + $1 = **$5**.
Ruth had $4 + $3 = **$7**.

2. Work backwards.
Let the number be ☐.
91.01 – 10.01 = 81
☐ × ☐ = 81
Since 81 = 9 × 9, Sally's number is **9**.

3. Observe that 2, 3, 4, 5, 6, 7, 8, 9, 10, 11, 12 are not factors of 377.
However, 13 is a factor of 377.
377 = 13 × 29
The two numbers are **13** and **29**.

4.
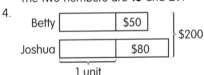
Betty $50

Joshua $80

} $200

1 unit

From the model,
2 units → $200 - $50 – $80 = $70
1 unit → $70 ÷ 2 = $35
Joshua had $35 + $80 = **$115** at first.

5.

|  | Short-sighted | Long-sighted | Total |
|---|---|---|---|
| **Number of boys** | 32 | **19** | **51** |
| **Number of girls** | **28** | 25 | 53 |
| **Total** | **60** | 44 | 104 |

Total number of boys = 104 – 53 = 51
Number of long-sighted boys = 51 – 32 = 19
Number of long-sighted girls = 44 – 19 = 25
Number of short-sighted girls = 53 – 25 = 28
Total number of short-sighted students
= 32 + 28 = 60

6.
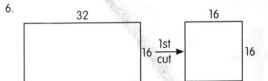

...

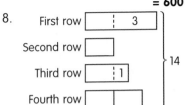

7th cut → $\square$2 2    8th cut → $\square$1 2

A total of **8** cuts are needed.

7. Surface area of one side of the square
= 5 cm × 5 cm
= 25 cm$^2$
There are 24 squares covering the surface of the solid.
Total surface area of solid = 24 × 25 cm$^2$
= **600 cm$^2$**

8.
First row ┆ 3

Second row

Third row ┆1

Fourth row

} 14

5 units → 14 – 3 – 1 = 10
1 unit → 10 ÷ 5 = 2
Number of coins in first row = 2 + 3
= **5**
Number of coins in second row = **2**
Number of coins in third row = 2 + 1
= **3**
Number of coins in fourth row = 2 × 2
= **4**

9. *Before*
Henry

Donald

*After*
Henry

Donald

35

7 units → 35
1 unit → 35 ÷ 7 = 5
10 units → 10 × 5 = 50
Number of pens Donald had at first = **50**

10. Area of triangles P and Q = Area of unshaded parts

Area Q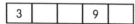

Area P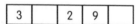

Area of unshaded parts = 3 units
Ratio = **1 : 3**

## Challenging Problems (pp. 178–182)

1. $252 = 2 \times 2 \times 3 \times 3 \times 7$
   Since the cards can only take numbers from 1 to 13, we look for three numbers, each not more than 13, whose product is 252.
   They are $2 \times 2$, $3 \times 3$ and 7.
   The three cards are numbered **4**, **7**, and **9**.

2. Clue (ii) implies that the 1st digit must be at least 3.

   Clue (iii) implies that the 1st digit cannot be 3 or more, because if this were so, the 4th digit would then be a 2-digit number. So the 1st digit must be 3, and the 4th digit must be $3 \times 3 = 9$.

   | 3 | | 9 | |
   |---|---|---|---|

   Clue (ii) and (iv) imply that the 3rd digit must be 2 – if it were 1, then the last digit would also be the same as the 2nd digit.

   | 3 | | 2 | 9 | |
   |---|---|---|---|---|

   Since the last digit must be a single digit number, the 2nd digit can only be 4 – it cannot be 2 or 3, because from clue (i), all the digits are different.
   So the number is

   | 3 | 4 | 2 | 9 | 8 |
   |---|---|---|---|---|

3. Suppose there were 6 girls and 3 boys. Then any of the 6 girls would have 5 sisters and 3 brothers, and any of the 3 boys would have 2 brothers and 6 sisters. But that does not satisfy the given condition.

   Suppose there were 5 girls and 2 boys. Then any girl would have 4 sisters and 2 brothers, and any boy would have one brother and 5 sisters. This satisfies the condition.

   Hence, there are **2 boys** and **5 girls**.

4. Suppose the pen costs 60¢.
   Since Alan needs 50¢ more, Alan only has 10¢.
   Since Amy needs 10¢ more, Amy only has 50¢.
   When they pool their money together, they would have a total of 10¢ + 50¢ = 60¢; this

is just enough to buy the 60¢ pen. Hence, the pen cannot be 60¢.

Suppose the pen costs 55¢.
Then Alan has only 5¢ and Amy has only 45¢. So the both of them have a total of 5¢ + 45¢ = 50¢.
This means that they still need 5¢ more to buy the 55¢ pen.
Therefore, the pen costs **55¢**.

5.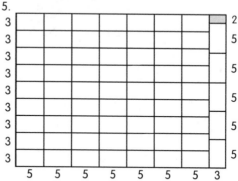

   7 small rectangles can fit along the length of the cardboard.
   9 small rectangles can fit along its breadth.
   5 small rectangles can fit vertically along the last 3-centimetre of the length of the cardboard.
   There is a total of $7 \times 9 + 5$
   = **68** small rectangles.

6. Length: $21 \div 1.5 = 14$ tiles
   Breadth: $12 \div 1.5 = 8$ tiles
   There are 14 tiles along the length and 8 tiles along the breadth.
   $(14 \times 8) \times 2 = 44$
   Robert will need a total of **44** square tiles.

7.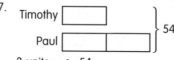

   3 units ⟶ 54
   1 unit ⟶ 54 ÷ 3 = 18
   2 units ⟶ 2 × 18 = 36
   Timothy's age this year = 18 years old
   Paul's age this year = 36 years old
   Difference in age = 18 years
   When Timothy is 36 years old,
   Paul's age ⟶ 36 + 18 = 54 years old
   Combined age ⟶ 36 + 54 = **90 years**

8. If there were 46 baskets of apples, the number of apples would be $46 \times 8 = 368$.
   So, the extra 560 – 368 = 192 apples were packed into boxes.
   One basket of apples had 12 more apples than one box of apples.
   So, there were 192 ÷ 12 = **16** boxes of apples.

9. $0.78125 = \dfrac{78{,}125}{100{,}000}$

   $= \dfrac{125 \times 625}{125 \times 800}$

   $= \dfrac{625}{800}$

   $= \dfrac{25 \times 25}{25 \times 32}$

   $= \dfrac{25}{32}$

   The two numbers are **25** and **32**.

10. *Method 1*

    Number of matches in the first round

    $= 32 \div 2$

    $= 16$

    Number of matches in the second round

    $= 16 \div 2$

    $= 8$

    Number of matches in the third round

    $= 8 \div 2$

    $= 4$

    Number of matches in the fourth round

    $= 4 \div 2$

    $= 2$

    Number of matches in the fifth round

    $= 2 \div 2$

    $= 1$

    Total number of matches that the winner played

    $= 16 + 8 + 4 + 2 + 1$

    $= \mathbf{31}$

    *Method 2*

    There are 31 losers, each having played a match. Hence **31** matches are played before there is a winner.

    *Note:* The winner plays 5 times.

Blank